HOLD EM'S

ODD(s)

BOOK

Mike Petriv

HOLD'EM'S

ODD(s)

BOOK

Mike Petriv

The Objective Observer   Toronto

HOLD'EM'S ODD(s) BOOK
Copyright (c) 1996 by Mike Petriv

Published in Canada by
The Objective Observer, Toronto.

ISBN 0-968-12230-2

First Edition
10 9 8 7 6 5 4 3 2 1

Typing and formatting by Lena Petriv

The Objective Observer
33 Beaucourt Road
Etobicoke, Ontario
Canada, M8Y 3G1
(416) 252-1876

To family,
who have remained constant
in their support, through my
numerous reinventions of self.

Part of the proceeds of this book go to the victims of Chernobyl.

TABLE OF CONTENTS*

* also see **DETAILED TABLE OF CONTENTS** next page

DETAILED TABLE OF CONTENTS

PART III

FOREWORD

Do you want to increase your hourly win rate? Then, read on. This is the primer and textbook on Hold'em probabilities that every winning player should own. Learn how to **calculate** probability and **apply** probability to gain an insider's edge. But, if the words probability and the gambling of mathematics have scared you in the past, **fear no more.** If you know how to multiply and divide, you can master the necessary aspects of this black art with ease. All you need is this book, a deck of cards, a calculator, and a mind that doesn't refuse to work. **But this book is much, much more.** We take the techniques which you learn in the first part of the book and apply it in the annexes to systematically and comprehensively analyze every probability aspect of this game. Then, just watch your hourly rate climb.

Hold'em has undergone a rapid expansion in the United States, Canada and Europe. It has brought hundreds of thousands of new players to public poker rooms. In Toronto, the new and temporary home of longshot poker, many of them play as if there was no such thing as probability. Maybe they don't know any better and maybe some of them don't care. To the former I offer this book. Needless to say, for the pros it's been easy pickings.

In going over my collection of poker books, I found very few that had decent tables on Hold'em probabilities; most were inadequate, some were inaccurate. None were **systematic** and **comprehensive**, and certainly none of them showed the reader how to calculate the odds for himself, except for the easiest and most obvious situations,

1

such as the odds against completing an open-ended straight draw on the turn. In short, the very **foundation** had been neglected.

I then turned to my books on probability. Here I read about permutations and Bernoulli's theorem and more $y= a(x-2n)$ equations than I could handle. And after all that, I still couldn't figure out how to calculate Hold'em probabilities for most situations.

Recently, I took a hard look at figuring out the odds and everything came together. The result is **HOLD'EM'S ODD(s) BOOK**, the encyclopaedia on this subject. It is for the player who would truly know this aspect, of this complicated game. The book is a simple, comprehensive, user-friendly, layman's approach to Hold'em probabilities. There are no leaps from obscure and irrelevant theory to difficult situations. Examples and short quizzes with solutions abound, as well as discussions on interesting topics like the running pair and handling improbability. By the end of this book, you will know how to approach any single-hand Hold'em probability and solve it. More importantly, you'll be making **informed** decisions every step of the way in your game, making and saving you dollars. Also, the intimate knowledge of probability which you gain from this book, should reduce your frustration and help to keep you from going on tilt. An added bonus is a beneficial increase in your reasoning ability. However, if you are like most people, who would rather die than think*, rather lose than win, this book may not be for you.

* A keen, if somewhat cynical, observation made by the philosopher Ayn Rand.

Foreword

A final thought- on any given day, at any given moment, the improbable triumphs over the probable, and appears to do so frustratingly often. But, over the long haul, luck gives way to the favorite. As Louis Pasteur said:

Chance favors the prepared mind

Michael Petriv
March 1996

INTRODUCTION

HOLD'EM'S ODD(s) BOOK, provides the reader with the gambling concepts, mathematical tools, and logical thinking required to solve Hold'em probabilities. It then applies that knowledge to come up with the most complete and systematic analysis of Hold'em probabilities - ever. It is written by a layman for the average player, in an easy to follow, step-by-step manner. This gentle approach does **not** come at the price of accuracy, completeness, or avoidance of difficult problems.

In chapter 1, **MATH REVIEW**, basic math operations with fractions and decimals are covered, as well as the order of operations. Covering basic math at this early point in the book allows us to maintain momentum later on when tackling more difficult work. If it's been some time since you last did math work, quickly go over the material and verify your understanding by doing the quiz at the end.

Odds indicate the extent to which we are gambling. In the chapter, **ODDS AND PROBABILITIES**, these concepts are explained. Then, using what was learned in, **MATH REVIEW**, we convert odds to probabilitiies and vice versa.

Chapter 3, **LAYING OUT THE CARDS**, starts with the composition basics of a deck of cards and moves from there to thinking about cards, not as 52 separate entities, but as combinations of cards. The game of Hold'em lends itself very well to analysis by combinations. This in turn, sets the conceptual framework for the chapter on **COMBINATIONS**.

In the chapter, **COMBINATIONS**, the reader

learns how to calculate the number of combinations which can be made from a given number of cards using one **simple** formula. This formula and some logical thinking applied on a case-by-case basis allow us to solve Hold'em probabilities.

In the chapter, **REFERENCE COMBINATIONS**, we determine the number of combinations for recurring situations such as the total possible number of two card combinations before the flop. Later, when solving simple and complex probabilities, and doing work in the annexes, these reference combinations will be used again and again.

In the chapters, **SIMPLE PROBABILITIES**, and, **COMPLEX PROBABILITIES**, the previous material is used to solve all manner of probability problems in a step-by-step manner. Three methods will be used: the universally applicable combinations method, and the more limited combined probabilities method, and its variant, the shotgun method. The latter two methods are used where applicable.

High speed computers and simulation programs have made it possible to easily determine the odds for multiple hands. In the chapter, **COMPUTER SIMULATION**, the computer and program are asked to determine the odds against pocket Queens beating pocket Kings, heads-up. The human process, though exact, is exceedingly long and difficult, and is only partially shown. The computer is the power tool of multiple hand probabilities and is king in this area. It represents the next step after the material in this book becomes foundation knowledge.

The second part of the book contains annexes and related appendices which comprehensively and systematically analyze the stages of Hold'em from pre-flop to river. We then do the same for the five types of starting hands: pairs, onsuit and offsuit cards, onsuit and offsuit connectors. These annexes and appendices will become a permanent and valuable reference. Finally, the poem, **A Gambler's Lament**, at the very end, will not be a harbinger of things to come if you study and learn this material well. Good Luck.

CONVENTIONS

Cards:
1. When dealing with cards, the small c,d,h, and s denote clubs, diamonds, hearts, and spades respectively. The small 's' may also indicate the plural of an abbreviation such as As or Ks, for Aces and Kings. The intended meaning is derived through context.
2. When not written out, capitals A,K,Q,J, and T denote Ace, King, Queen, Jack, and Ten respectively.
3. ff where used, denotes two cards of the same suit.

English:
1. When a single digit number stands alone, it will be spelt out, e.g., "six cards" not "6 cards". A single digit standing alone implies the rank of the card, i.e., 7 means the card of that rank.
2. Where clarity is not an issue, the plural of the rank will be abbreviated: Aces may be written as As, Tens as Ts, etc.
3. American spelling over Canadian and English.
4. The abbreviation for, "that is", is ,"i.e.", and, "for example", is, "e.g."
5. Since this is a detailed step-by-step presentation of Hold'em probabilities, and I intend to hold your hand all the way, I will talk in terms of you, we, our, etc.

Poker Terminology:
1. The terminology is standard as applies to Hold'em. The board means the community cards. The flop is the first three community cards, the fourth card is the turn, and the last card is the river. Your two card

starting hand is sometimes referred to as your hole cards.

2. To have a set, means to have a pair in your hand and another of the same rank on the board. Only one player can have a set.

3. To have trips, means to have two different ranks in your hand, and two of either rank on the board. Two players may have trips. Trips also mean three of the same rank on the board.

4. The term "odds" always implies the "odds against something happening", with the odds against always being the first number.

5. In this book, when referring to starting hands, the term, offsuit cards, means exactly what it says, and also means cards of different ranks.

Mathematical:

1. Multiplication in this book is indicated by "*" and NOT "." or "x". Multiplication is also implied by a number preceding or following brackets, e.g., 5(3+8), means multiply the sum of the numbers contained in the brackets by five. Answer:55

2. Division in this book is indicated by /.

3. Decimal point numbers will be rounded off to intelligible numbers. If the odds are 330.5:1, that number will be rounded off to 331:1. If the probability of something happening is .00003, the number will become 0. These numbers will usually be found in the tables at the back of the book. In the discussion preceding each table, the more exact number will most often be found. See DECIMAL POINT NUMBERS in the chapter, **MATH REVIEW**, for instruction on how to round off numbers.

PART I

Learning

MATH REVIEW

If you are comfortable with the order of arithmetic operations, multiplying, reducing, and cancelling in fractions, decimal numbers and converting to percentages and fractions, the inverse of a number, solving for an unknown number where two fractions equal each other, and rounding off decimal numbers, proceed to the next chapter or breeze over the quiz at the end of this chapter.

ORDER OF OPERATIONS
To correctly solve math problems, the convention is to do multiplication and division first as they occur, that is, take the number left of the sign and the number right of the sign and solve. Then do addition and subtraction. If the equation contains brackets, (), the operations indicated within the brackets must be done first.

Examples:

a) 3+5*4= 3+20= 23

b) 8/2+3-5= 4+3-5= 2

c) 5*(4+2)= 5*6= 30

d) 9/(2+1)*4+2= 9/3*4+2= 3*4+2= 14

FRACTIONS
For the fraction 3/5, (read three fifths or three over five) the top or leading number is called the numerator, i.e., 3. The trailing or bottom number is called the denominator, i.e., 5. To multiply fractions

11

together, multiply the top parts or numerators together, and multiply the denominators together. See the examples below.

A fraction remains the same value if you multiply the top and bottom by the same number. Likewise, dividing the top and the bottom by the same number does not change its value. See examples below. The purpose of dividing the top and bottom by the same number is to reduce the fraction to a smaller value. This is called reducing a fraction to its lowest common denominator. For a more complex fraction having several numbers in the numerator which need to be multiplied together and several numbers in the denominator which need to be multiplied together, the process can be made simpler by cancelling. In cancelling for example, a 5 in the numerator and a 5 in the denominator can both be stroked out.

Examples:

a) 4/52= 1/13. The first fraction was reduced by dividing the top and bottom by 4. The chances of getting an Ace as your first card are 4/52 or 1/13.

b) 3/5*2/4= 6/20= 3/10. The two fractions were multiplied together, 3*2/5*4 and the answer was reduced by dividing top and bottom by 2 to get 3/10.

c) 4/52*3/51= 1/13*1/17= 1/221. Here we reduced each fraction separately. For 4/52, we divided top and bottom by 4 to get 1/13 and for 3/51, we divided top and bottom by 3 to get 1/17. We then multiplied the fractions together, 1*1 and 13*17 to get 1/221.

d) 8*6*4*2/6*3*2= 8*4/3= 32/3. Here the 6s and the 2s in the top and bottom were cancelled out.

e) 8*3/16*9= 1/2*3= 1/6. Here the 8 and 16 were reduced by dividing each number by 8, and the 3 and 9 were each divided by 3 leaving 1*1/2*3= 1/6.

DECIMAL NUMBERS
Here I mean numbers such as 1.55, .01, .001, etc. My math friend, Frank G., tells me that strictly speaking, this is an incorrect designation.

Probabilities are expressed as decimal numbers or as percentages. To convert a decimal number to a percentage multiply by 100. See examples a and b. To convert a percentage to a decimal number divide by 100. See examples c and d. To convert a decimal number to a fraction, multiply the top by a number needed to move the decimal place over to get a whole number. Use that multiplier as the denominator. See examples e and f. To convert a fraction to a decimal number, divide the top by the bottom. See examples g and h.

Examples:

a) .1= .1*100= 10%

b) .25= .25*100= 25%

c) 87%= 87/100= .87

d) 33%= 33/100= .33

e) .23= .23*100 and using the 100 as the denominator gives 23/100.

f) .984= .984*1000 and using the 1000 as the denominator gives 984/1000.

g) 3/4= .75

h) 472/1000= .472

ROUNDING OFF DECIMAL POINT NUMBERS

In our later work, we will frequently end up with numbers like 4.0892, which when rounded off to one decimal place, becomes 4.1. This number will often make more sense then the strictly, more exact correct number. The general rule for rounding off is to count .05 and above as .1, and any number .049 or below as .0, if rounding off to one decimal place. Often, the size of the number will dictate how we round off the number: 330.5 will become 331, .008 will become .01.

THE INVERSE OF A NUMBER

The inverse of 2 is 1/2, the inverse of 5 is 1/5, the inverse of .2 is 5, the inverse of .5 is 2. To get the inverse of a number, divide 1 by the number. See examples below.

Examples:

a) 8. The inverse of 8 is 1/8

b) .6. The inverse of .6 is 1/.6= 1.66 with the 6 repeating.

UNKNOWN QUANTITY

On the odd occasion, it will be necessary to solve for an unknown quantity. In the example of $4/5= u/10$, u is the unknown quantity. Diagonally multiply the quantities across the equal sign: doing so gives us $4*10= 5*u$ or $40= 5u$. When a number is moved across an equal sign, the opposite operation is done. Taking 5 across it becomes division. Therefore, $40/5= u$ and $u= 8$.

Examples:

a) $1/3= u/27$ becomes $3u= 27$ becomes $u= 27/3$ and $u= 9$.

b) $1/8= u/64$ becomes $8u= 64$ becomes $u= 64/8$ and $u= 8$.

c) $1/221= u/1326$ becomes $221u= 1326$ becomes $u= 1326/221$ and $u= 6$.

MATH REVIEW QUIZ (answers at back of book)

1. $(1225-1081)/1225=$?
2. Reduce the following fractions to their lowest common denominator: $16/1326$ and $2304/19600$. Convert the fractions to decimal numbers.
3. $50*49*48/3*2*1=$?
4. $52*51*50*49*48/5*4*3*2*1=$?
5. Convert .35 and .0084 to percentages.
6. Convert 31.5% and .03% to decimal numbers.
7. Round off the following to one decimal place: 1.86 and 2.76.
8. Solve for the unknown quantities x and u: $x/1326= 1/221$ and $u*969= 15504*64$.

ODDS AND PROBABILITIES

When I first started playing poker and read some books, most authors included a table on odds and probabilities for certain Hold'em situations. The table typically had two columns: one was titled "**Odds**" and the other was titled "**Probability**". To the left of the columns was a description of what the odds against and probability were for some event happening, such as a pocket pair improving to a set, full house or quads on the flop. Under "Odds" it said "7.5:1" (read as seven and half to one). Under "Probability" it said ".118" or "11.8%". **Both are variations on the same theme and are two ways of stating the chances of something happening.** If the odds are known, the probability can easily be calculated and vice versa. Why complicate life by stating something two ways? Each has its merits and differences as we shall see.

ODDS

Odds give you the bad news up front, in unavoidable black and white; they are brutally honest. When dealing with Hold'em poker, as in the case above, the odds tell the player that he will probably **MISS** improving 7.5 times for every **one** time that he does improve. No fun. On the other hand, **probability**, by stating the chances of improving as a decimal number or %, tells you the same thing, but in a way that is less direct, less honest, i.e., you will improve 11.8% of the time; it declines to mention that you will not improve 100−11.8= 88.2% of the time. The odds against improving are 88.2:11.8= 7.5:1.

By convention, the first number states

how many times something will not happen, while the second number states how many times it will happen. Usually the second number is reduced to 1. If both sides of the odds equation are multiplied by the same number, the equation remains the same. Multiplying both sides by two, we have 7.5*2= 15 and 1*2= 2 and our odds equation is now 15:2 (read as fifteen to two), which is exactly equal to 7.5:1. To express the odds in the form x:1, divide both sides by the number on the right. For example, take 20:5, divide 20 by 5 and 5 by 5 to get 4:1.

One reason why many players talk in terms of odds is because they can relate their chances of improving their hand to the size of the pot, i.e., compare their odds against improving to the dollar odds which the pot is offering them. This becomes a primary consideration on whether to fold, call, raise, or reraise. For example, if you have flopped a nut four flush draw, the odds against completion are 1.86:1. If the game was 10-20, and there was $60 in pre-flop, and the flop was triple raised before getting to you for an additional 10+20+30= $60 more, the pot total would now be 60+60= $120. If you intend to call for $30, the pot is offering you $120 for your $30, or $4:$1, on a situation where the odds against you are only 1.86:1. In such a situation you must call, or reraise on the come, as long as you aren't drawing dead.

Another reason to talk in terms of odds, is that it makes more sense in some situations because of the magnitude of the numbers. For example, the odds against being dealt pocket Aces are 220:1 or 1/221= .0045= .45%. I find 220:1 to be more user-friendly.

In playing Hold'em, decisions are constantly being made. In looking at your starting hand, say TJ, you might expect to flop an open-ended straight draw **and** complete it on the turn or river. The likelihood of success would be expressed as, what is the probability of making a straight by the turn or river, if an open-ended straight is flopped. If the odds against are known for each of the two events, it is **NOT** possible to directly multiply the odds together to get the odds against making a straight (it can be done only after converting the odds to the probability of improving). But, using probabilities expressed as decimal numbers, it is a straightforward multiplication. To summarize, the downside of using odds are that it is inconvenient when trying to figure out a situation where an outcome depends on more than one event happening. However, once that outcome is determined, the probability can easily be converted into odds. For example, if you hold two suited cards, the probability of flopping a four flush is 11%. The probability of making a flush by the river is 35%. The probability of making a flush in this way is the combined probabilities of both events happening, i.e., .11*.35= .039= 3.9%. To convert this probability to odds, realize that if the flush will be made 3.9% of the time, then 96.1% of the time it will not be made. The odds against making the flush as described are 96.1:3.9. Dividing both sides by 3.9, we get approximately 25:1.

PROBABILITY
Probability, as relates to Hold'em poker,

tells the player the chances of an event happening in terms of a fraction, a number, or a percentage. The odds against making at least a set on the flop when holding a pocket pair are 7.5:1. The probability is 1/8.5, .118, or .118*100= 11.8%. The odds against completing a four flush are 1.86:1. The probability is 1/2.86, .35, or .35*100= 35%. To convert odds to probability, take the number on the left, put it underneath the number on the right and add to it the value of the number on the right. For example, the odds are 15:2. To convert to probability using the method just described, we have 2/(15+2)= 2/17= .118= 11.8%.

Probability, by using numbers or fractions, allows the player to calculate the chances of success where an outcome depends on a previous event happening (also known as a parlay in other betting activities). The probability of getting an Ace as your first card is 4 in 52, or 4/52. The probability of getting a second Ace is 3 in 51, or 3/51. The probability of getting pocket Aces is the product or multiplication of the two probabilities which is 4/52*3/51= 12/2652= .004525 or .4525%.

But, that small percentage is difficult to relate to, which brings us back again to converting probabilities to odds and vice versa. The probability of getting pocket Aces is .004525. The probability of not getting pocket Aces is 1-.004525= .995475. Now we have the two numbers needed for the odds equation, .995475:.004525. As discussed in the paragraph on odds, the player needs to divide both sides by the right side to get the odds expressed in the form x:1. Doing so with the above two numbers we get

.995475/.004524= 220:1. If the probability is expressed in terms of a fraction, such as 4/52*3/51 for getting pocket Aces, then by reducing we get 1/13*1/17= 1/221. In this form we can convert to odds by doing the reverse of converting odds to probability, i.e., (221-1):1, or 220:1.

For me, saying that the odds against completing a four flush are 1.86:1, is more difficult to remember than stated as a probability of 35%. As we delve deeper into odds and probabilities in the annexes section of the book, you may find that it is more convenient to think in terms of one or the other for certain situations.

In the introduction to this book I stated that the player would be shown how to determine odds and probabilities by the use of combinations for all cases, and where applicable, by the other method sometimes known as the helping and non-helping card method (combining of probabilities). A thorough knowledge of the above material is required when we get to that section of the book. Finally, if the player is uncomfortable with the above manipulations and calculations, seek assistance.

ODDS AND PROBABILITIES QUIZ

The probability of getting a pocket pair as your hole cards is 1/17. The odds against getting a pocket pair are _____:_____. The odds against getting at least a set on the flop are 7.5:1. The probability of improving to at least a set is _____%. With an open-ended straight draw and one card to come, you have eight outs in the remaining 46 cards. The odds against making the straight are ___:___. The probability of making the straight is _____%. The probability of getting suited cards before the flop is 23.5%. The odds against it are _____. The odds against flopping a flush are 118:1. The probability of it happening is_____.

LAYING OUT THE CARDS

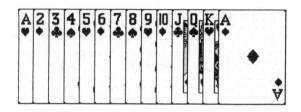

This chapter asks us to think about a
deck of cards and see them in terms of
combinations, as opposed to 52 separate
entities. By chapter's end, the reader will
be receptive to learning about how to
calculate the number of combinations in
order to solve probability questions. Access
to the world of probability is gained
through learning how to think in terms of
combinations and through learning how to
quantify combinations.

Pull out a deck of cards and strip away
the non-essentials such that we have 52
cards. From the deuce to the Ace, we have 13
ranks of four suits each. Now lay out 14
cards of mixed suits in sequence from Ace,
deuce, 3, 4, ...Ace. Starting from left to
right, and taking the cards five at a time,
we find that there are 10 different
straights. Substitute any of the cards with
the same rank, but of a different suit, and
we end up with different straights. How many
different straights can we make? Plenty, as
this substitution process could go on for a
long time.

Go through the same process with suited
cards and make the Ace do double duty at
both ends. Counting, there are 10 straight
flushes possible for that suit. Grab the
four Jacks and look at the remaining 48

cards. Each one of those 48 cards can form the fifth card of a poker hand. That makes 48 different poker hands of quad Jacks. Now grab three 9s. Grab a pair of 4s and you have 9s full of 4s. Substitute one of the 9s in your hand with the remaining 9. You have a different set of trip 9s in your hand and a different 9s full. Substitute one of the 4s, or grab a different pair. Again, more 9s full. So many combinations, so many possibilities.

Turn the cards over and take any two. An Ace of diamonds and a two of clubs- uh, what a combination. Discard the deuce and take another. Ah, the Jack of hearts and you feel better. Discard that Jack and pull another- bah, an eight of spades. If we did this for a while, we would exhaust all the two card combinations for an Ace of diamonds and that number would be 51 combinations. If we took the Ace of spades and did the same exercise, we'd end up with only 50 different combinations, because one of those combinations would have already been seen: the Ace of diamonds and the Ace of spades. If we now take the Ace of clubs and do the same exercise, we'd find that we'd be going over the same ground when we paired it with the Ace of diamonds and the Ace of clubs, and the only different combination would be with the Ace of hearts, leaving only 49 new two card combinations. Finally, if we take the Ace of hearts, we see that there are no new Ace combinations, but we can combine the Ace of hearts with the 48 other cards. There does seem to be an orderly and regular decline in the number of combinations. How many two card combinations are there? We don't know at this point, except that it seems to be a long and difficult process to sort out and remember all those combinations. Wouldn't it be convenient if we could easily calculate the number of AA combinations, and maybe at the same time calculate all the possible two card combinations in a deck of 52 cards, rather than laying it all out by hand? Of course it would be.

There is a way, it's easy, and the results yield very useful information on probabilities. If we knew the total possible number of two card combinations for a deck of 52 cards, and knew that six of the total two card combinations were Aces, the probability of getting pocket Aces would simply be six divided by the total possible number of two cards combinations. If we also knew how many combinations of AK there were, we would have a basis on which to assess whether the raise from the rock on the right is more likely to indicate pocket Aces or an AK. Then we could decide whether we should call with our pocket Kings.

Now, take that deck of cards and give yourself pocket Queens. Shuffle the remaining 50 cards and then flop three cards. Damn, an Ace, a King, and a deuce. Pull back the flop, reshuffle and flop again. Damn, a King, a Ten, and a 9. Do it again. This time there are no overcards but the flop is 7, 8, and 9, all spades, and you've got the red Queens. You could do this all day and keep getting a different three card combination. Eventually, you'd get a Queen on the flop and your pulse would pick up. Keep doing it and eventually you'd flop two Queens and your pulse would race. But, it would take a long time to determine all the possible three card combinations with 50 different cards. Finding out the number of three card combinations containing a Queen or two Queens, although easier, would still be difficult. If we were asked to determine all the possible five card poker hands in a deck of 52 cards, the task would be near impossible by laying out the cards, even with all the King's horses and all the King's men. If only there was some quick way to calculate all those combinations. Well there is, and that leads us to the next chapter on ......

COMBINATIONS

ABOUT COMBINATIONS

This is the key concept and technique we use in determining Hold'em probabilities. The **combination formula** which we are about to learn is a **quick and exact** method for counting the number of combinations which can be made from a larger number of cards. For example, we can determine the number of five card poker hands, i.e., the number of five card combinations, which can be made from a deck of 52 cards relatively quickly. **Without** the combination formula, we would have to resort to laying out all the possibilities, all 2,598,960 five card hands, **by hand**, a near impossible feat. **But,** with the quick count method we are about to learn, the determination of the number of combinations, and hence probability, becomes easy and practicable.

In books on probability, the combination formula is usually covered in a section dealing with permutations and combinations. In permutations, the order of cards would make a difference: the flop AsKsQs is not the same as QsKsAs. Since they are both the same in Hold'em, permutations are irrelevant to our purposes and so I will say no more on the subject of permutations. Now to the much more understandable and relevant concept of combinations.

Combinations are ideally suited to the solving of Hold'em probabilities. Why? Because 5/7ths of our hand come directly in the form of combinations: our two card combination **starting hand** and our three card combination **flop**. After the flop, the turn and river, although coming individually, can be viewed as a combination when deciding whether to call and continue into the more expensive rounds. All Hold'em probabilities can be solved, in the main, by determining the number of desired combinations and comparing that to the total number of possible combinations. The probability, or odds against improving, can then be compared to the **pot odds** to **guide** us in our actions. This will become clear shortly.

To illustrate the usefulness of knowing the number of combinations, look at the following example. For now, just accept that the number of combinations is correct. Before the flop, each player holds two cards. The total possible number of two card combinations is 1326. Of that total, the number of possible AA combinations is six. Therefore, there are 1326-6= 1320 **non AA** combinations. Lay them out if you don't believe me. The chances of getting pocket Aces before the flop are six in 1326, or 6/1326. Converting that to odds, we have (1326-6):6 or 1320:6, and dividing both sides by six, we have the odds against getting pocket Aces as **220:1**. And there you have the **basic** technique for solving Hold'em probabilities by combinations: determine the number of combinations of interest and compare that to the total number of combinations. Later on, I will show you the thinking needed to solve more complex probabilities, and I will show you how to solve certain types of probability problems by other methods as applicable.

CALCULATING THE NUMBER OF COMBINATIONS

Now that we have glimpsed how useful combinations can be, let's find out how to calculate the number of combinations. In our thinking about combinations, we ask how many ways can the smaller number of cards which we are interested in be combined compared to a larger number of combinations, which, for Hold'em, is the number of combinations which can be made from the remaining unknown cards in the deck.

Let's look again at the pocket Aces before the flop. The cards of interest are the four Aces, which can be combined in pairs in a number of ways. We ask ourselves, how many ways can four Aces be combined into different two card combinations? The answer is 4*3/2*1= 12/2= 6. There are six different AA combinations. The total possible number of different two card combinations in a deck of 52 cards is 52*51/2*1= 1652/2= 1326, i.e., there are 1326 possible starting hands. Can you figure out the formula for determining the number of combinations?

First, determine the number of cards in the desired combination: before the flop it is two, for the flop it is three, for the turn **and** river it is two, for the board it is five. Take the number of interest and put it in the denominator, or bottom or trailing part of the equation. Multiply that number down until you end up with one. For example, two is 2*1, three is 3*2*1, five is 5*4*3*2*1. The numerator, or top or leading part of the equation becomes the number of cards of interest. Multiply it down until you have the same number of numbers as in the denominator, or bottom, or trailing part of the equation. For example, if we were looking for a three card combination, the denominator or bottom is 3*2*1. If the number of cards of interest is 50, the numerator or top becomes 50*49*48. **Both top and bottom now have three numbers each and are balanced.** Multiply and divide out to get the number of combinations, i.e., the number of three card combinations which can be made from 50 cards. See the paragraph below for the answer. There it is, the combination formula plain and simple. It need not get any more complex, and doesn't in this book. For those wishing to know more on the subject of combinations, there are numerous books on probability to choose from.

In dealing with probability on the flop, we first need to determine how many different three card combinations (**flops**) can be made from the remaining 50 cards. The answer is 50*49*48/3*2*1= 19600 (note that there are three numbers on top and three numbers on the bottom). There are 19600 different three card combinations (**flops**) possible from the remaining 50 cards (you hold two cards in your hand). You follow up that determination by asking how many of those three card combinations contain cards which are of interest to you. For example, if you hold pocket 7s before the flop, how many flop combinations contain one or two 7s? Once that number is determined, you can calculate the probability of flopping a set or quads.

The above combination formula is the key to solving Hold'em probability questions. The more complex probability problems will require a little thinking, but there will be plenty of examples worked out to give the reader the general idea.

DISCUSSION

This is a basic book. Part I endeavors to teach how to determine probability by the use of combinations. All of the probability situations are approached from a single player's point of view. With my starting hand and 50 cards remaining, the flop will go **one** of **19600** ways. The truth is, if the game is 10-handed, there are only 52-20= 32 cards, not 50, remaining. How do we resolve this discrepancy? Does it mean our approach is wrong? **Absolutely not.** As long as there are 50 cards which are **unknown** to you, the flop will be **one** of **19600** that are possible. However, if the cards which you would like to see are held by other players and/or the deck is stacked (shuffled) in a way that goes against you, the flop will be a disappointment, i.e., one of the many other thousands of flops that are possible.

COMBINATIONS QUIZ
1. Determine the total possible number of five card flushes which can be made from the 13 spades.
2. You are holding your two hole cards. With the remaining 50 cards, determine the total possible number of five card combinations.

REFERENCE COMBINATIONS

HOLD'EM'S ODD(s) BOOK, PART I, has a narrow focus, i.e., to teach the player how to determine probability in Hold'em. This narrow focus is of great benefit, because it allows the player to learn how to competently and confidently use combinations, and develop correct thinking. In doing so, certain combinations keep coming up over and over again. These are our reference combinations, and they will most often form the denominator or bottom of the probability fraction we eventually end up with. If you can't see it now, don't worry, it will become readily apparent in our later work. Most of these combinations are work-related, while others are more of a trivia-type in nature. Why differentiate between the two? Because, most often when playing, your concerns will be more worldly: how likely is it that the rock who just raised has pocket Aces or AK, and then, after seeing a flop, deciding on whether to commit more money in the hopes of improving your hand with two more cards to come. These micro-figurings are done against the grand backdrop of the huge number of possibilities in poker, which are covered in the trivia section. Note that there are no reference combinations from flop to turn and turn to river. For these one card situations, you only need to determine the number of outs, and then put that number over the total cards remaining and calculate the probability of it happening.

WORK-RELATED REFERENCE COMBINATIONS

Before the flop reference combinations:

a) Determine the total possible number of **two card** combinations with a deck of 52 cards.
Solution: 52*51/2*1=2652/2= 1326
That number is the total of **all** the pocket pairs in **all** their possible combinations, **all** the suited two card combinations, and **all** the unsuited card combinations.

b) Determine the number of ways any rank, e.g., four Jacks, can be combined into pairs.
Solution: 4*3/2*1= 6
This means that there are six different JJ combinations: JcJs, JcJd, JcJh, JsJd, JsJh, and JdJh.

On the flop reference combination:

Determine the total possible number of three card combinations from the remaining 50 cards.
Solution: 50*49*48/3*2*1= 117600/6= 19600
This means that with your two specific cards in hand, you will get one of a possible 19600 flops.

From the flop to the river reference combination (two cards to come):

Determine the total possible number of two card combinations which can be made from the remaining 47 cards (two in your hand and three on the flop, leaving 47).
Solution: 47*46/2*1=2162/2= 1081

This means that your hand will end up with one of the possible 1081 two card combinations.

Other useful reference combinations:

a) Determine the number of ways any rank, e.g., the four Tens, can be combined in trips.
Solution: 4*3*2/3*2*1= 24/6= 4.
This means that there are four different TTT combinations: TcTsTd, TcTsTh, TcTdTh, and TsTdTh.

b) Determine the number of ways the 7s, 8s, and 9s can form non-tripping and non-pairing, i.e., three card 789 sequences.

Solution: There are 12 cards in total. The number of three card combinations which 12 cards can make is 12*11*10/3*2*1= 1320/6= 220. Some of those combinations are trips, and some are pairs. We must determine those numbers and subtract them from 220. The number of trips for any rank is 4 (see the work above). The total number of trips for the three ranks is 3*4=12. The number of pairs: any rank can make six pairs, and any of those six pairs can combine with any one of the other eight cards from the other two ranks. The number of 778 and 779

33

combinations is 6*8= 48. The same is true for the 887 and 889 combinations, as well as the 997 and 998 combinations. The total number of pair plus card combinations is 3*48= 144. The total number of pair plus card and trip combinations is 144+12= 156. The number of 789 sequences (any order) is 220-156= 64.

A very quick approach is 'sequence logic' as follows: each of the 7s may combine with each of the 8s, for 4*4= **16** 78 combinations; each of those 16 combinations can combine with each of the 9s, for a total of 16*4= **64** 789 combinations, or 4^3= 64.

Or, as long as we know the total number of combinations (220), we can use the **combined probabilities** method to verify our work above. Start with any of the 12 cards as our first card. The probability of not pairing with the second card from the remaining 11 cards, is 8/11. If the first and second cards are not paired, then there are six cards in total from the remaining 10 cards which will pair the first two cards and so the probability of **not pairing** is 4/10. The overall probability of not pairing is 8/11*4/10= 32/110. The number of non-tripping and non-pairing combinations is x, where x/220= 32/110, and cross-multiplying gives 110x= 220*32. Dividing both sides by 110, gives x= 220*32/110= 64. We have confirmation.

A note about using the method of **combining probabilities** versus using combinations. Where it can be used, and it is **not** universally applicable, it often takes less time to arrive at the solution. It is somewhat like taking a jet from Toronto to Vancouver, or New York to Los

Angeles: you get there a lot faster than in a car, but you miss a lot of the (in)sights along the way.

TRIVIA-RELATED REFERENCE COMBINATIONS

The numbers which we derive below, show us the incredible number of possibilities with 52 and 50 cards combined in different ways. Those possibilities are the raw material for a great game. That, plus the money aspect, explains in part, our never-ending fascination with this game.

a) Determine the total possible number of five card poker hands which can be made from a deck of 52 cards.
Solution: 52*51*50*49*48*/5*4*3*2*1= 311,875,200/120= 2,598,960.
For the odds against hitting any type of hand in **five** cards, see the table, **HAND RANKINGS**, in Annex J.

b) Hold'em is a **seven** card game, where the best **five** card hand wins. Determine the total possible number of seven card combinations from a deck of 52 cards.
Solution:
52*51*50*49*48*47*46/7*6*5*4*3*2*1= 2,598,960*47*46/7*6=   5,618,951,520/42= 133,784,560.
Notice that by going from 5 to 7 cards, the number of possible combinations has jumped from 2,598,960 to 133,784,560, an increase of approximately 51 and a half times. Note that the number of five card poker hands remains the same and always will: you've just increased your probability of hitting them by giving yourself seven cards.

Real Trivia: If you played Hold'em every day of the year, and you played 30 hands per hour for eight hours a day to the river, you would have played 87,600 hands in the course of that year. The minimum number of years required to see all the possible seven card combinations would be 133,784,560/87600= 1,527. Life is short.

c) After you have received your two hole cards, there are still five cards to come. Determine the total possible number of five card combinations from the remaining 50 cards.
Solution: 50*49*48*47*46/5*4*3*2*1= 254,251,200/120= 2,118,760.

A final thought: poker imitates life, and as the blinkered lib-left critic would caricature it, poker imitates life at its capitalist worst- **the winner takes all.**
As the cards are being shuffled and we sit there adjusting our baseball caps, shades, and headphones, a vast universe of more than 133 million possible hands await (seven cards to come). At the river, each remaining player will have his own one of those more than 133 million possibilities, **but**, we are getting ahead of ourselves. Before the deal, all players start with an equal chance to make a big hand. But, the deck is stacked: most often our cards will not play themselves and each player will have to decide whether to continue on in an increasingly shrinking universe. Better thinking will make for better decisions, giving better results. This will be true of course, if Lady Luck doesn't have a crush on someone else. The first decision the player

will make, is whether to continue with the one of 1326 possible starting hands he is dealt. As he looks at his hole cards, he realizes that with five cards to come and 50 cards remaining, things will go one of 2,118,760 ways. If he decides to continue, his future, in large measure, will hinge on one of 19600 flops that are possible with his two hole cards and the remaining 50 cards. If he decides to continue after the flop, his world will become much smaller. With 47 remaining cards and only two to come, his fate will be sealed by the one of 1081 possible two card combinations that end up being dealt. At the end, with seven cards to draw from, he will be left with only one of a possible 2,598,960 poker hands, and it will be compared to someone else's one of a possible 2,598,960 poker hands, and any others who have stayed and paid to the river. And then....**the winner takes all**. At that point, the lib-left critic will mock earnestly ask, **"What about social justice?"**, as he scoops in another massive pot and cracks a banana-wide smile.

SIMPLE PROBABILITIES

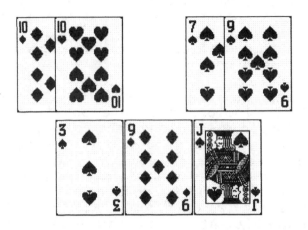

In this chapter, simple probabilities will be solved through the use of combinations, combined probabilities, and, shotgunning where possible, for hole cards, the flop, turn, and river. Differentiation is made between simple and complex probabilities, because a simple probability is a fairly straightforward proposition. In complex probabilities, we will need to use logic and our knowledge of poker to strip away combinations which are not of use. The combinations method will always be used first, because it is universally applicable, and because it shows the inner workings of probability, as well as the inherent richness and diversity of poker hands.

The techniques which we learn in the following problems will be applied in the annexes portion of the book to give a complete, detailed, and systematic treatment of Hold'em probabilities for all the types of starting hands and all the stages of the game.

HOLE CARDS

Problem #1
Determine the odds against getting pocket Kings before the flop.

Using combinations:
Approach: Determine the total possible number of two card combinations in a deck of 52 cards. Then determine the number of possible KK combinations. Manipulate the two numbers to determine the probability and odds of getting pocket Kings. Confirm the correctness of the answer by using the combined probability method.
Solution: The number of possible two card combinations in a deck of 52 cards is 52*51/2*1= 2652/2= 1326. The number of possible KK combinations, i.e., two card combinations from four cards, is 4*3/2*1= 12/2= 6. The probability of getting pocket Kings before the flop is 6/1326= 1/221 or

.0045 or .45%. The odds against getting pocket Kings are (1326-6):6= 1320:6, and dividing both sides by six, we get 220:1. If you ask what the odds are against getting any specific pair before the flop, the answer will be the same.

Using probabilities:
Solution: The chances of getting a King as your first card are 4 in 52 or 4/52, or dividing top and bottom by four, 1/13. Assuming we are dealt the one King, there are 51 cards left, three of which are Kings. The chances of getting another King are 3 in 51 or 3/51, or dividing top and bottom by three, 1/17. The probability of getting pocket Kings is obtained by multiplying the probabilities of both Kings coming, or 1/13*1/17= 1/221. The odds against getting pocket Kings are (221-1):1= 220:1.

Problem #2
Determine the odds against getting a pocket pair before the flop.

Using combinations:
Approach: Determine the total possible number of two card combinations in a deck of 52 cards. Then, determine how many different pair combinations a rank can make, the four deuces for example. Take that number and multiply by the thirteen ranks (2s to Aces). Compare the total number of pairs to the total possible number of two card combinations for 52 cards.
Solution: The total possible number of two card combinations for 52 cards is 52*51/2*1= 1326. The number of possible deuce pair combinations is 4*3/2*1= 6. The total number

of pair combinations for 52 cards is the number of ranks (13) times six, or 13*6= 78. The probability of getting a pocket pair is 78 in 1326, or 78/1326, or dividing top and bottom by 78, 1/17. The odds against getting a pocket pair are (17-1):1= 16:1.

Using probabilities:
Solution: We are dealt any card as our first card, say a 7. To make a pair of 7s from the remaining 51 cards, we must hit one of the three remaining 7s. The probability of doing so is 3/51 or 1/17. The odds against getting a pocket pair are (17-1):1= 16:1.

Problem #3
Determine the odds against getting suited cards before the flop.

Using combinations:
Approach: Determine the total possible number of two card combinations in a deck of 52 cards. Then, take one suit, hearts for example, and determine the total possible number of two card combinations for the 13 hearts. Multiply that number by four to get the total possible number of two card, suited combinations and then solve.
Solution: The total possible number of two card combinations for 52 cards is 52*51/2*1= 1326. The 13 hearts (from 2-Ace) can make 13*12/2*1= 156/2= 78 two card suited combinations. The four suits can make 4*78= 312 two card, suited combinations. The probability of getting suited cards before the flop is 312/1326= .235= 23.5%. The odds against getting suited cards are (1326-312):312= 1014:312= 3.25:1.

Using probabilities:

Solution: Start by receiving any card. The chances of getting one of the 12 remaining cards of the same suit, from the remaining 51 cards are 12/51= .235= 23.5%. The odds against getting suited cards are (51-12):12= 39:12= 3.25:1.

Problem #4

Determine the number of unique value pre-flop hands.

Background Note: After you have learned the material in this book, you will naturally move on to probabilities for multi-way action. In those books, they recognize many fewer than the 1326 different pre-flop hands. For the purpose of their computer simulations, non-suited hands such as KcJh, KsJd, KdJh, and KhJs, etc., are all the same value prior to the flop. With suited cards, KhQh is the same as KsQs, is the same as KdQd, is the same as KcQc. The flop may make them different. For pocket pairs, AsAh is the same as AcAd, is the same as AhAc, etc., prior to the flop. Summarizing, they recognize pairs, onsuit, and offsuit combinations.

Using combinations:

Approach: Determine the number of suited two card combinations for one suit. Then, by deduction, the number of non-suited two card combinations is exactly the same. To that, add the thirteen pairs.

Solution: The number of possible two suited card combinations for one suit is 13*12/2*1=156/2= 78. The number of possible two card, non-suited combinations is also 78. The number of pairs is 13. The number of different value hands before the flop is 78+78+13= 169.

FLOP
The flop consists of three cards. With two cards in your hand, there are 50 cards remaining. The total possible number of three card combinations with 50 cards is 50*49*48/3*2*1= 19600 (see, **REFERENCE COMBINATIONS**, for further detail). This combination will be frequently used in the following flop probabilities.

Problem #1
Determine the odds against flopping a set, full house, or quads when holding pocket deuces.

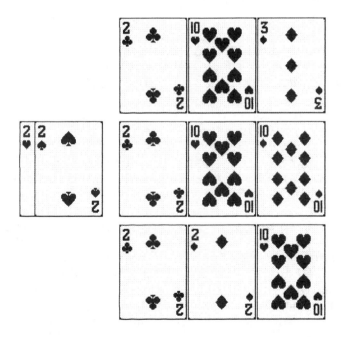

Using combinations:

Approach: Determine the total possible number of three card combinations for the remaining 50 cards when you hold two deuces in your hand. Then determine the number of those flop combinations which contain a single deuce. Then determine the number of those combinations which contain two deuces. To determine the odds of flopping a set, full house, or quads, add the combinations and solve.

Solution: The total possible number of three card combinations from the remaining 50 cards is 50*49*48/3*2*1= 19600. To get a set of deuces, or a full house, the flop must fit the following model: xx2, where xx can be any of the remaining cards which are not deuces. Since the deuces are excluded, there are 48 cards which can be used for the xx part. The total number of two card combinations which can be made from the 48 cards is 48*47/2*1= 2256/2= 1128. Either of the two remaining deuces may combine with any of the 1128 combinations, giving 2*1128= 2256 combinations which contain a deuce. The probability of hitting a set or full house is 2256 in 19600, or 2256/19600. The odds against hitting a set or full house are (19600-2256):2256, or 17344:2256= 7.688:1. or, a probability of 2256/19600= .115, or 11.5%.

To hit quads, the flop must fit the following model: x22, where x is any of the remaining 48 cards (52 minus the four deuces). Since there is only one deuce deuce combination possible, the number of three card combinations containing deuce deuce is 48. The odds against hitting quads on the flop are (19600-48):48, or 19552:48, or

407:1. The probability of hitting quads is 48/19600= .003= .3%

The number of combinations which give a set, full house, or quads is 2256+48= 2304. The odds against hitting a set, full house, or quads are (19600-2304):2304= 17296:2304, or 7.51:1. The probability is 2304/19600= .118, or 11.8%.

In the annex, **THE POCKET PAIR**, we break the flop down to the number of set and full house combinations.

Using probabilities:
Note: Here we run into a limitation when using combined probabilities. With this method, we cannot break the problem down into the component probabilities of sets, full houses, and quads. The figure which we derive is the probability of hitting a set, full house, or quads on the flop, often expressed in other books as the probability of improving to "at least a set".
Approach: Determine the probability of not getting any deuces on the flop.
Solution: The probability of not hitting any of the two deuces in the remaining 50 cards is 48 in 50, or 48/50, or 24/25. If we don't hit a deuce, the probability of not hitting a deuce with the second card of the flop and with 49 cards left is 47/49. If that condition is met, we will not hit a deuce with the remaining 48 cards, 46 out of 48 times, or 23/24. The probability of not hitting a set, full house, or quads is the combined probabilities, or 24/25*47/49*23/24= 1/25*47/49*23/1 (we cancelled out the 24 on top and bottom)= 1081/1225. The probability of hitting a set, full house, or quads is (1225-1081)/1225=

144/1225= .118= 11.8%. The odds against it are (1225-144):144= 1081:144= 7.51:1.

By shotgunning:
Some people will use the following reasoning: I have two outs (the two deuces) and three chances to hit at least one. Therefore, I have six chances out of 50 to improve my hand. The odds against it are (50-6):6= 44:6= 7.3:1. That's pretty close, it's fast, but slightly understates the odds.

Problem #2
Determine the odds against flopping two of your suit, if you start with a suited hand (hearts for example).

Using combinations:
Approach: Determine the total possible number of three card combinations. Then, determine the total possible number of three card combinations which contain two of your suit. Manipulate and solve.
Solution: The total possible number of three card combinations which can be made from 50 cards is 50*49*48/3*2*1= 19600. The total number of three card combinations containing two of your suit, fits the model xhh, where x is any of the remaining 50 cards which are not hearts, i.e., 50-11=39. With 11 hearts remaining, the total possible number of two card heart combinations is 11*10/2*1= 110/2= 55. Each of those 55 two heart card combinations may combine with any of the remaining 39 cards. Therefore, the number of three card combinations which contain two hearts is 55*39= 2145. The probability of making a four flush on the flop is

2145/19600= .109= 10.9%. The odds against making a four flush are (19600-2145):2145= 17455:2145= 8.14:1.

Using probabilities:
    This type of problem cannot be solved by this method.

By shotgunning:
    This type of problem cannot be solved by this method.

FLOP TO TURN

Problem #1
Determine the odds against making a flush on the turn, when holding a four flush.

Solution: After the flop there are 47 unseen cards, of which 13-4= 9 are the flush cards of interest. The probability of making a flush on the turn is 9/47= .19= 19%. The odds against making a flush on the turn are (47-9):9= 38:9= 4.2:1

Problem #2
Determine the odds against completing an open-ended straight on the turn.

Solution: After the flop there are 47 unseen cards, of which eight will make your straight. The probability of making a straight on the turn is 8/47= .17= 17%. The odds against it are (47-8):8= 39:8= 4.9:1.

TURN TO RIVER

Determine the odds against making a full

house or quads on the river when you have made a set, say 7s, on the flop.

Solution: After the turn, the model is xy7z, with 46 cards remaining. To make a full house or quads on the river, you can hit the one remaining 7, or either of the three Xs, Ys, or Zs; that gives you 10 outs. The probability of improving is 10/46= .2174= 21.7%. The odds against it are (46-10):10= 36:10= 3.6:1.

FLOP TO RIVER
In this situation, we look at the odds against the hand improving with two cards to come.

Problem #1
Determine the odds against making a flush by the river with a four flush on the flop.

Using combinations:
Approach: With four flush cards so far, there are nine of the desired suit in the remaining 47 cards. There are two cards to come. Determine the total possible number of two card combinations with 47 cards, and then determine the number of two card combinations which make a flush. Manipulate and solve.
Solution: With 47 cards remaining, the total possible number of two card combinations is 47*46/2*1= 2162/2= 1081. A certain number of those two card combinations make flushes. For example, if we are on hearts, then two running hearts will make a flush, or a non-heart and heart combination, or a heart and non-heart combination. As far as the final

strength of your hand, the heart/non-heart, and non-heart/heart combinations are both the same.

With nine hearts remaining, the total number of two heart combinations is 9*8/2*1= 72/2= 36. That part is done and covers the probability of two running hearts. Of the 47 remaining cards, 47-9= 38 are cards of the three other suits. Any of the nine hearts may combine with any of the 38 other cards, giving us 9*38= 342 heart/non-heart combinations. The total number of flush-making combinations is 36+342= 380. The probability of making the flush is 380/1081= .352= 35.2%= 35%. The odds against making a flush are (1081-380):380= 701:380= 1.85:1 .

Using probabilities:
Approach and solution: To determine the probability of making a flush, we must approach it by determining the odds of not making a flush. The chances of missing your flush cards are 38/47*37/46= 1406/2162= .6503= 65%. Your chances of making the flush are 100-65= 35%.

Using probabilities yielded a quick solution. However, had we asked for the probability of hitting only one flush card, or hitting two flush cards, it would not have been possible.

By shotgunning:
With 47 cards remaining, nine are flush cards. With two cards to come we have 9*2=18 outs. The probability of making a flush is 18/47=.383= 38.3%. We are close with this method, but overly optimistic by 3.3%. Still, that's not bad.

Problem #2
Determine the odds against completing an open-ended straight draw on the flop, by the river. Assume the open-ended straight draw is 9TJQ of different suits.

Using combinations:
Approach: There are 47 remaining cards, eight of which will make the straight (four 8s and four Ks). Determine the total possible number of two card combinations with 47 cards to come. Then, take the 8s and Ks together, and determine the number of two card combinations which they can make (88, 8K, KK, etc.). Then, strip out the 8s and the Ks, and determine the number of combinations which the remaining cards can make with each of the 8s and Ks. Manipulate and solve.

Solution: The total possible number of two card combinations which can be made from 47 cards is 47*46/2*1= 1081.

The four 8s and four Ks can make 8*7/2*1= 56/2= 28 different two card combinations, each of which will complete the straight (some will make a Q high straight, i.e., 88, some will make an 8 to K high straight, i.e., 8 and a K, and some will make the K high straight, i.e., KK. Note that of those 28 combinations, there are six 88 and six KK combinations which could destroy your hand. That part is done.

Now to the single 8 and single K combinations. Removing the 8s and Ks from the 47 remaining cards leaves us with 39 non-straightening cards. Each of those may combine with either of the 8s and either of the Ks, giving us 39*8= 312 more straightening two card combinations.

50

Simple Probabilities

The total number of two card combinations which complete the straight are 28+312= 340. The probability of completing an open-ended straight draw with two cards to come is 340/1081= .315= 31.5%. The odds against completing the straight are (1081-340):340= 741:340= 2.18:1= 2.2:1.

Using probabilities:
Approach: Determine the probability of making the straight by determining the probability of missing the eight cards on the turn and river.
Solution: The chances of missing an eight or a King with the turn card are (47-8)/47= 39/47. The chances of missing an eight or a King on the river are (46-8)/46= 38/46. The probability of missing the straight is 39/47*38/46= 1482/2162. The probability of making the straight is (2162-1482)/2162= 680/2162= .315= 31.5%. The odds against making the straight are (2162-680):680= 1482:680= 2.18:1= 2.2:1.

By shotgunning:
I have eight outs and two shots at making it. Therefore, I have 8*2= 16 outs, out of 47 remaining cards. The probability of making the straight is 16/47= .34= 34%. The odds against making the straight are (47-16):16= 31:16= 1.94:1. Close, but overly optimistic.

Comment: A few words on the method of combinations versus the combined probabilities method: for those situations where combined probabilities can be used, and their application is not universal, the solution is arrived at more quickly.

However, the process is not very revealing. In the example above, using combinations, we see that there are 12 pair combinations which will make our straight, but which could also make someone a full house. The combinations method is to be preferred for the complete picture which it gives.

Finally, some advanced books on Hold'em will contain a chart which shows the percentage chance of completing a hand with two cards to come for any number of outs. The technique for arriving at the answers is not shown. With what we have learned it should be rather easy to derive the answer.

Problem #3
Verify that with 10 outs after the flop, you will complete your hand 38.4 % of the time.

Using combinations:
Approach: Determine the number of two card combinations for 47 cards, and then determine the number of two out combinations for 10 outs (hitting two of your outs), and the number of two card combinations containing only one out. Manipulate and solve.
Solution: The number of two card combinations with 47 cards is 47*46/2*1= 2162/2= 1081. The number of two out combinations for 10 outs is 10*9/2*1=45, i.e., you can make your hand 45 different ways by hitting two of your ten outs. The number of single out combinations is the number of non-out cards multiplied by the number of outs, i.e., (47-10)*10= 37*10= 370. The total number of combinations which will complete your hand is 370+45= 415. The probability of making one or two of your

outs is 415/1081= .384= 38.4%.

Using probabilities:
Solution: With 47 cards remaining, the probability of missing one of your outs is (47-10)/47= 37/47. If you miss one of your outs, there are 46 cards remaining. The probability of not hitting one of those outs is (46-10)/46= 36/46. The probability of not hitting any of your outs is 37/47*36/46= 1332/2162. The probability of hitting one of your outs is (2162-1332)/2162= 830/2162= .384= 38.4%

By shotgunning:
With 10 outs and two shots to complete my hand, I have 20 outs. The chances of making it are 20/47= .426= 42.6%. Well, fairly close.

In the annex, **TWO TO COME**, there is a general purpose table for any number of outs, which shows in detail the complete numbers and situations for this stage of the game, i.e., the likelihood of hitting one, two, and one **or** two of your outs.

SIMPLE PROBABILITIES QUIZ

1. With four outs to make your hand, and two cards to come (the case for an inside straight draw, or two pairs to improve to a full house or quads), determine the probability of making your hand.
2. Holding two suited cards, determine the probability of flopping a flush.
3. With AQ in your hand, determine the probability of flopping quad Queens.

COMPLEX PROBABILITIES

This chapter carries on from the previous chapter. Whereas the previous probabilities were rather straightforward in their solution, the following problems require more thought and logic.

HOLE CARDS

Problem #1
Determine the probability of getting AK.

Using combinations:
Approach: Determine the total possible number of two card combinations for 52 cards. Then, we must think about the problem. There are four Aces and four Kings, giving us a total of eight cards out of 52. Combining the As and Ks will give us a certain number of AA and KK combinations, as well as AK combinations. The number of pair combinations must be stripped out to arrive at the number of AK combinations.
Solution: The total possible number of two card combinations for 52 cards is $52*51/2*1=$ 1326. The number of two card combinations which the eight cards of interest can make is $8*7/2*1= 56/2= 28$. But now we have to stop and do some thinking. Of those 28 combinations, some will be AA and KK. The number of these combinations must be

determined and subtracted from 28. For the four Aces, the number of AA combinations is 4*3/2*1= 6; the same is true for the Kings. Therefore, there are 6+6= 12 AA and KK combinations. The number of AK combinations is 28-12= 16. The odds against getting an AK before the flop are (1326-16):16= 1310:16= 81.875:1= 82:1. The probability of getting AK before the flop is 16/1326= .012= 1.2%.

Using probabilities:
Approach: This relatively easy problem can be solved by combining the probability of hitting either an Ace or King on the first card, and then hitting the other rank as the second card.
Solution: The chances of hitting an Ace or a King as the first card are 8 in 52, or 2 in 13, i.e., 2/13. If the first card is an Ace or a King, the chances of hitting the other rank are 4 in 51, there being one less card from the deck of 52. The probability of getting an AK is the product of the probabilities of the first and second events happening, or 2/13*4/51= 8/663= .012= 1.2%. The odds against it are (663-8):8= 655:8= 81.875:1= 82:1.

Problem #2
Determine the odds against two players both holding pocket Aces.

 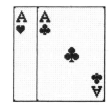

Using combinations:

Approach: Consider the two players holding pocket Aces to be one player holding quads. Then, determine the number of possible four card combinations with 52 cards. Of that number of combinations, only one will be four Aces.

Solution: The total possible number of four card combinations with a deck of 52 cards is 52*51*50*49/4*3*2*1= 6,497,400/24= 270725. The probability that two players will hold pocket Aces is 1/270725. The odds against two players holding pocket Aces are 270724:1.

Alternate solution by using combinations:

Approach: Two players flip over pocket Aces. Determine the probability of one player getting pocket Aces, then, with 50 cards remaining, of which two are Aces, determine the number of two cards combinations for 50 cards, of which only one is pocket Aces, and multiply the probabilities together. Although this approach requires more work, it has greater application which we will see later on in the annex, **TORONTO HOLD'EM.**

Solution: The probability that the first player will end up with pocket Aces is 1/221 (as determined before in, **SIMPLE PROBABILITIES**, with pocket Kings). For the second player, there are only 50 cards left, of which two are Aces. That makes one, two card combination containing Aces. The total possible number of two card combinations for 50 cards is 50*49/2*1= 2450/2= 1225. The probability that the second player will get pocket Aces is 1/1225. The probability that two players will have pocket Aces is 1/221*1/1225= 1/270725. Voila.

Using probabilities:
Approach: Combine the probabilities of hitting all the Aces.
Solution: The probability of hitting the first Ace is 4/52= 1/13; the probability of hitting the second is 3/51; for the third it is 2/50= 1/25; and for the fourth it is 1/49. The combined probability is 1/13*3/51*1/25*1/49= 3/812175= 1/270725.

FLOP

Problem #1
Determine the probability that there will be no card higher than a 7 on the flop, when two players are holding pocket eights.
Note: The 8s are the median rank. There are six ranks above (24 cards), and six ranks below (24 cards).

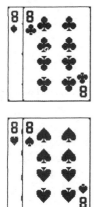

Using combinations:
Approach: Determine the total number of three card combinations for 48 cards (the deck minus the four 8s). Then determine the number of three card combinations which the 24 cards below 8 can make. Subtract that number from the total number of three card combinations. The remainder will be the number of three card combinations which contain **either** one, two, or three cards 9 or higher.
Solution: The total number of three card combinations which can be made from 48 cards is 48*47*46/3*2*1= 103776/6= 17296. The lower six ranks (24 cards) can make 24*23*22/3*2*1= 12144/6= 2024 three card combinations. By definition, those combinations will have no card higher than a 7, and all other combinations will have **either** one, two, or three cards which are higher than an 8. The probability that the flop will contain cards 7 and below is 2024/17296= .117= 11.7%. The odds against this happening are (17296-2024):2024= 15272:2024= 7.55:1.

Using probabilities:
Approach: Determine the probability of hitting a card 7 or under. Then determine the probabilities that the second and third cards will also be 7 or under. Multiply the probabilities together for the answer.
Solution: With 48 cards, the probability that the first card will be a 7 or under is 24/48. If it is, the probability that the second card will be 7 or under is 23/47 (23 small cards, 24 big cards, total of 47 cards). If it is, the probability that the third card will be 7 and under is 22/46 (22

small cards, 24 big cards, total of 46 cards). The probability that all three cards will be 7 and under is 24/48*23/47*22/46= 12144/103776= .117= 11.7%.

By shotgunning:
Approach and solution: Half the cards (.5) are above the 8s, and half are below. The chance of hitting a low one is .5, as it is for the second and third card. Shotgunning, we have .5*.5*.5= .125= 12.5%, which counts when using a shotgun.

Problem #2
Determine the odds against flopping a straight when holding Jack Ten offsuit as your starting cards.

Using combinations:
Approach: First, determine the total possible number of flops for the 50 remaining cards. Then, determine which three card combinations result in a straight, and determine the number of combinations for each possibility. Multiply, manipulate, and solve.
Solution: The total possible number of three card combinations for 50 cards (the two cards JT are in your hand) is 50*49*48/3*2*1=117600/6= 19600. The

combinations which flop a straight are 789, 89Q, 9QK, and QKA. Now, we must determine the number of combinations for each sequence that give the straight. To do so, we will look at 789 first. There are 12 cards, and the number of ways 12 cards can be made into three card combinations is 12*11*10/3*2*1=1320/6= 220. But that number contains trips and pair combinations which must be determined and stripped out.

The four 7s can make 4*3*2/3*2*1= 4 combinations of 777. The same holds true for the 8s and 9s. Therefore, there are 3*4= 12 trips, or three of a kind combinations which are non-straightening. The other non-straightening combinations are of the type 778, or 887, or 989, etc. The number of these type of combinations must be calculated. Here's the approach. Take the 7s: the four 7s can be combined into how many combinations of 77. The answer is 4*3/2*1= 6. Each of those six 77 combinations can have any of the 8s or 9s (eight cards in total) as the third member of the three card combination on the flop. This gives 6*8= 48 non-straightening three card combinations of the type 77x. The same is true for the 8s and the 9s, giving a total of 3*48= 144 non-straightening combinations containing two of the same rank.

We are ready to solve. There are a total of 144+12= 156 non-straightening combinations of the total possible 220 three card combinations which can be made from the 12 cards. Therefore, the number of 789 straightening combinations are 220-156= 64. For the sequence 89Q there would also be 64 straightening combinations. The same holds true for 9QK, and QKA. Therefore, the total number of three card straightening combinations is 4*64= 256. The total number of three card combinations for 50 cards is 19600, of which 256 give a straight on the flop. Therefore, the odds against flopping a straight are (19600-256):256= 19344:256= 75.6:1= 76:1. The probability of flopping a straight is 256/19600= .013= 1.3%.

Flopping a straight with AK is only possible with TJQ, or 64 combinations. The probability of that happening is 64/19600= .0033= .33%

Using probabilities:
This problem cannot be directly solved by combining probabilities. The best we can do is to calculate the probability that there will be no pair or trips in 12 cards and confirm that section of the combinations work above.
Approach: Take one straightening combination, say 789, and determine the probability of making no pair or trips.
Solution: There are four 7s, four 8s, and four 9s from which to make three cards which do not contain a pair or trips. After the first card has fallen, say an 8, the second card can be any 7 or any 9, but not an 8. The probability of this happening is 8/11. Assume the second card is a 9. The third card from the remaining 10 cards must be one of the four 7s, and **not** one of the three remaining 8s or three remaining 9s. The probability of that is 4/10. The probability that there will be no pair or trips is 8/11*4/10= 32/110= .291= 29.1%

Now if we knew that there were 220 possible three cards combinations, then we could say the number of three card straightening combinations is .291*220= 64. The same would hold true for the other three card combinations giving 4*64= 256 straightening combinations. If we knew that there were 19600 possible three card combinations from 50 cards, we'd know the probability of flopping a straight to be 256/19600= .013= 1.3%.

Problem #3
Determine the total number of TJQKA straights possible from a deck of 52 cards. Also, determine the total number of all the straights (including straight flushes) possible.

Using combinations:
Approach: Determine the total possible number of five card combinations with 20 cards. Determine and strip out all the fours of a kind, full houses, trips, two pairs, and pair combinations, leaving the number of straights and straight flushes.
Solution: The total possible number of five card combinations from 20 cards is 20*19*18*17*16/5*4*3*2*1= 1,860,408/120= 15504.

　　　　Quads. There are the five types (Ts, Js, Qs, Ks, As), each of which may be combined with any of the 16 other cards, e.g., QQQQ combines with each of the four Tens, each of the four Jacks, etc. Therefore, the total number of quad five card combinations is 5*16= 80.

Full Houses. Here we must determine the number of combinations that fit into the xxxyy mold, where the Xs are cards of the same rank, and the Ys are a different rank pair. Each rank, the Tens for example, can make four different combinations of three of a kind, i.e., 4*3*2/3*2*1= 4. Each of those TTT combinations can be paired with all the possible pairs from the Js, Qs, Ks, and As. For any rank, there are 4*3/2*1= 6 pair possibilities. For Js to As there are 4*6= 24 pair possibilities. The Tens can make 4*24= 96 different types of full houses from the 20 cards we are looking at. Since each rank will have the same possibilities, the total number of full houses is 5*96= 480.

Trips. The number of onboard trips, xxxyz, where the Xs are the same as in the example above, can be combined with yz, where Y and Z are all the possible two card combinations which **do not** make a pair. As before, each rank can make four different three card combinations of itself, i.e., 4*3*2/3*2*1= 4. For example, there are four different TTT combinations. The total possible number of two card combinations which the other 16 cards can make is 6*15/2*1= 120. Those 120 combinations include pairs, so we must strip them out. Each of the Js, Qs, Ks, and As can combine into six different pair combinations. Therefore, the total number of pair combinations is 4*6= 24, and 120-24= 96. The total number of yz combinations is 96.

Finally, the total number of onboard trips for the tens is 4*96= 384. Since the same is true for every other rank, there are 5*384= 1920 different, five card trips combinations.

Two Pairs. The number of two pair five card combinations is represented by xxyyz. Each rank can make six different pair combinations. Taking one pair combination of the Tens out of the possible six, we see that it can combine with any of the other 24 pair combinations of Js, Qs, Ks, and As. For all six pairs of TT, there are 6*24= 144 pair pair combinations. Each of those pair pair combinations can combine with either of the remaining 12 z cards, giving 16*144= 1728 TTyyz combinations.

It gets a bit tricky here. For the Jacks, there are six JJ combinations. When we calculated for all the TTxxy combinations, we covered all the possible TTJJy possibilities. Therefore, the six JJ combinations can only combine with the Queen, King, and Ace pair combinations which total 6*3= 18. The number of JJxx combinations (excluding the Tens which have already been accounted for) is 6*18= 108. Each of those combinations can have as its fifth card, the y, any of the remaining 12 cards. The total number of new five card combinations is 108*12= 1296 JJxxy, where xx cannot be Tens. You've got the idea now. For the Queens, there are six QQ combinations. Each of those QQ combinations can combine with the Kings and Aces to produce unaccounted for QQxxy combinations. The Kings and Aces each have six different pairs combinations. Therefore, the number of QQxx combinations are 6*12= 72, where xx cannot be TT or JJ. Each of those 72 combinations can have any of the remaining 12 cards as the fifth card giving 72*12= 864 QQKKy and QQAAy combinations.

The Kings can only uniquely combine with the Aces. Here we have the six KK and six AA combinations giving 36 AAKK combinations. Each of those combinations can have any of the 12 remaining cards as its fifth card. The total number of KKAAy combinations is 36*12=432.

For the Aces, all the two pair combinations have already been accounted for.

The total number of two pair combinations fitting the mold xxyyz is the sum of the above two pair combinations, i.e., 1728+1296+864+432= 4320.

One Pair. The one pair five card combination model is xxyzw, where xx is a pair, and yzw are different ranks from xx and are such that yzw cannot be three of a kind or a pair. The total number of pair combinations for the five ranks is 5*6= 30. Any pair can combine with any three card combination from the remaining 16 cards which does not contain a pair or trips. We must determine the number of those combinations and then strip out the trips and pair combinations. The total possible number of three card combinations from 16 cards is 16*15*14/3*2*1= 3360/6= 560. The total number of trip combinations which the four ranks can make is 4(4*3*2/3*2*1)= 4(4)= 16. The total number of pair combinations from the four ranks is 4*6= 24. Any one of those pairs can combine with either of the 12 cards from the remaining three ranks, giving 24*12= 288 three card combinations containing a pair. The total number of three card combinations containing a pair or trips is 16+288= 304. The total number of yzw combinations of three different ranks is 560-304= 256. The total number of five card pair combinations is 30*256= 7680.

The total of all the above is 80+480+1920+4320+7680= 14480.
The total number of combinations for five cards is 15504. Of that number, 14480 are not straights or straight flushes, so that the number of straights and straight flushes is 15504-14480= 1024. Four of those 1024 are Royal flushes, leaving 1020 straights which are beaten by flushes.

That was an involved process using combinations which yielded much other valuable information. There is an alternative approach using combinations which is quicker and simpler.

Alternative Approach using combinations:
Approach: Determine the number of JT combinations from the four Js and four Ts. Determine the number of QKA combinations from the four Qs, four Ks, and four As. Multiply the two together. In this way, we can use answers from work previously done.
Solution: The number of JT combinations is the same as the number of AK combinations, which we know to be 16. In the chapter, **REFERENCE COMBINATIONS**, we calculated the number of 789 combinations from all the 7s, 8s, and 9s, to be 64. The same will be true for the Qs, Ks, and As. Now, each JT combination may combine with each of the QKA combinations giving 16*64= 1024 straight flushes and straights. Quickest of all is sequence logic: 4*4*4*4*4= 4^5= 1024.

Using probabilities:

Approach: Determine the probability of hitting cards which do not pair the previous cards. Then use the total possible number of five cards combinations from 20 cards to solve.

Solution: Start with any of the 20 cards, say a Ten. Of the 19 remaining cards, we must hit a J or a Q or a K or an A, but not one of the three remaining Tens. The probability of not hitting a Ten is 16 out of 19 or 16/19. If this happens, say we hit a King, we have two parts of the straight and six cards (the three remaining Tens and the three remaining Kings) of the remaining 18 which we don't want to hit on the next card. The probability of hitting a card which doesn't pair the board is 12 out of 18 or 12/18. If this happens (say we hit a Jack), we have three parts of the straight and nine cards of the remaining 17 (the three Tens, the three Kings, and the three Jacks) which we don't want to hit for the fourth card of our straight. The probability of hitting a card which doesn't pair the board is 8 out of 17 or 8/17. If this happens, say we hit an Ace, we have four parts of the straight and 12 cards of the remaining 16 (the three Tens, the three Kings, the three Jacks, and the three Aces) which we don't want to hit for the fifth card of our straight. The probability of hitting a card which doesn't pair the board is 4 out of 16 or 4/16. The probability of making a straight is the product of the probabilities, i.e., 16/19*12/18*8/17*4/16. Reducing where possible prior to multiplication gives us

16/19*2/3*8/17*1/4=   16*2*8*1/19*3*17*4=

32*8/57*17*4= 32*2/57*17=
64/969. To determine the number of
straights, u, put u over the total number of
five card combinations which is 15504, and
make that equal to the probability of
hitting a straight, i.e., u/15504= 64/969.
Cross multiplying, u*969= 15504*64 and u969=
992256, making u= 992256/969= 1024. There
are 1024 TJQKA straights; four of those 1024
straights are Royal flushes. The number of
1024 equally applies to bicycle straights as
well as all the other straights. Determining
the total number of straights will be easy
and straightforward. There are ten types of
straights (A to 5, 2 to 6, 3 to 7, etc.)
giving 10*1024= 10240. Of that number, 40
are straight flushes giving 10200 straights
which are beaten by flushes.

COMPLEX PROBABILITIES QUIZ

1. Determine the odds of making trips on the
flop, i.e., two cards of the same rank on
the flop that match either of your hole
cards.
2. While holding pocket Aces, one of the
remaining Aces is flashed and is no longer
available. Calculate the odds against making
a set of Aces, or Aces full on the flop.
3. Of 2,598,960 possible five card
combinations, determine the number of full
houses.
4. **Petriv's Paradox:** The total possible
number of two card starting hands is
52*51/2*1= 1326. With your two cards in
hand, there are 50 remaining cards in the
deck. With the 50 cards remaining, the total
possible number of flops is 50*49*48/3*2*1=

19600. It follows then, with 1326 possible starting hands each having 19600 possible flops, there must be 1326*19600= 25,989,600 different five card hands. But, with a 52 card deck, we have already calculated the total possible number of five card combinations to be 52*51*50*49*48/5*4*3*2*1= 2,598,960. That number is only one tenth of the other number. Which answer is correct and why?

5. Determine the probability of flopping a four flush and a pair with AQ of clubs, as depicted in the situations below.

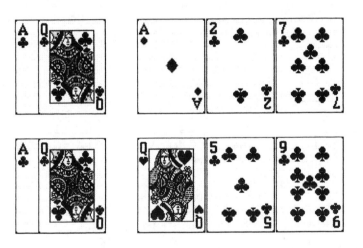

6. With AK of spades, determine the probability of flopping a flush, or a straight, or, a four flush only, or a four flush and a pair, or a pair without a four flush, i.e., some kind of hand. Disregard two pair and higher possibilities for now. Then, fill in the blank with one of the words enclosed in the brackets: AK suited is a _____ (favorite, dog) to flop a hand.

COMPUTER SIMULATION

By now, you will have noticed that most of the Hold'em probabilities have confined themselves to a single hand: the probability of getting a specific starting hand, and the probabilities of it improving on the flop, through to the river. This has been done in a vacuum: at the table, we will have to contend with other players and the strength of their hands, not to mention their tactics and numerous other factors as well. We have also calculated the total possible numbers of certain hands, like straights and flushes. Achieving this modest goal has been work, but it, along with the work to be done in the annexes, will form the solid foundation upon which our Hold'em game is built. The process and knowledge gained, cannot help but give those of us who are also perceptive and disciplined enough to be winners, a razor's edge advantage in defeating our opponents, while contributing thousands to the bottom line in dollars earned and dollars saved.

The next logical step would be to learn more about how well certain hands play against other hands: a very dynamic process, even when excluding human players. For these probabilities, we must put aside the pencil and calculator, and look to the computer and its high speed simulation programs. In these types of situations, we consider a hand's chances of improving, not in isolation, but as compared to one or more other hands with their own individual chances of improvement. Also, we look at all the ways in which hands may win, as well as tie, over the course of many deals and tally up the results. These multi-hand simulations are the subject of other books. But, before leaving our work in probability, I would like to compare the results of a computer simulation and the partial attempt at a manual solution, in order to demonstrate the role which the computer has to play in determining probability.

POCKET KINGS VS POCKET QUEENS

Recently, I played in a game of 10-20 Hold'em with some fairly consistent winners. The following situation arose: a player, David, raised in mid-position with pocket Queens and another player, Steve, two positions to his left, reraised with pocket Kings. All the other players folded, and David, the one with the pocket Queens, called. The pot now stood at 5+10+30+30= $75. The two players were friends, and David asked the other player if he would check it to the end. Steve agreed and they both flipped over their hands. Before the dealer acted, David, holding the red Queens, offered the following deal: give me back $5 and the pot is yours right now. Steve, with the black pocket Kings agreed and that was that. Another player, Frank, a math teacher and local poker legend, said to the player with the Queens, that he wasn't that much of a dog to lose the hand (70:5 or 14:1). At this point, both David and Steve heatedly disagreed with Frank and said the Queens were a tremendous dog. As they spoke, I realized that neither of the players involved could get beyond the fact that, since both hands had an equal chance to improve to sets, the Queens had virtually no chance of winning. Offhand, I didn't have the answer either, so I went home and did a great number of simulations with Mike Caro's, **Poker Probe**, program. The results, shown at the end of this chapter, surprised me, initially. I then tried to prove the simulation results by doing a hand calculation. It became a tremendous amount of work and easily convinced me of the overwhelming advantage of the computer and a good simulation program for dealing with **multi-hand probabilities**. My partial solution proved extremely revealing about how and why underdogs win, which is one of the reasons why poker is such a fascinating game.

MANUAL ATTEMPT
Problem: Determine the odds against the red Queens beating the black Kings in a heads-up confrontation taken to the river.
Approach: a) calculate the number of five card combinations which can be made from the remaining 48 cards (52 less the red Queens and black Kings),
b) determine the number of combinations where neither the Kings nor Queens win (ties),
c) determine the number of combinations where the Queens beat the Kings,
d) add the number of ties and the number of Queen wins and subtract that from the total

possible number of hands which can be made from 48 cards to arrive at the number of Kings' wins. The Kings' wins to Queens' wins give the odds against the Queens beating the Kings.

Solution:

a) **Five card combinations.** The number of five card combinations which can be made from 48 cards is 48*47*46*45*44/5*4*3*2*1= 1,712,304. That was easy.

b) **Ties:**

i. **On board quads.** Four of a kind from deuces to Jacks with one of the four Aces or one of the two remaining red Kings as a kicker result in ties. That gives 10 ranks. Either of the four Aces or either of the two red Kings, as kickers give 10*6=60 ties. Quad Aces with either of the two red Kings as kickers, also result in ties. Therefore, there are 62 quad ties.

ii. **On board full houses.** Take three of a kind from deuces to Jacks and pair them with the Aces and all the ties for full houses are covered. Each rank of four cards can make 4*3*2/3*2*1=4 different three of a kind combos. The Aces can make six different AA combinations. The number of full houses resulting in a tie is 10*3*6=180. Note that if we put three Aces on the board, the pocket Kings would give the better full house, so no tie there.

iii. **On board trips.** There are no on board trips that result in a tie, because the pocket Kings will give a higher full house than with the pocket Queens.

iv. **On board two pairs.** There are no two pair tie combinations.

v. **On board straights.** Many of the possible 10 board straights result in a tie. From A to 5 and 6 to 10 (six straights), all the cards are available to make straights, and all result in ties. The number of different straights for each straight is 1024 (this includes straight flushes). For the six straights with all the cards, there are 6*1024= 6144 straights and straight flushes resulting in ties. Note that all 7 to J on board straights will be won by the pocket queens which will make higher straights, except for the black straight flushes which will be ties, giving only two more ties. The 7 to J straight red flushes will be won by the red Queens which will make higher straight flushes. If an 8 to Q straight ends up on board, the Kings will win by making a higher straight, and will win the black straight flushes. On board red straight flushes are not possible. Because there are two Queens and two Kings in players hands, the number of different on board straights for 9 to K, and T to A will be reduced, but these also result in ties. There are 364+364=728-4 (on board straights that will become straight flushes)=724 more ties.

The number of ties (I hope) is 62+180+6144+724=7110.

c) **The Queen wins.** By determining the number of combinations where the Queens win and adding that to the number of ties, we can arrive at the number of combinations where the Kings win, i.e., the total number of combinations (1,712,304) less ties and Queens' wins. In general, the Queens will win when they improve to a set and the Kings don't (but even here, a Queen is no guarantee, because there can be quads on board, trips on board, a Queen high straight, a four straight where the King will be boss, black four flushes except QsQcBBB, black flushes etc.) when the Queens improve to quads and the Kings don't improve to a set, and when the Queens improve to quads while the Kings improve to a set. There are other straight situations as well; all 7 to J straight situations, and 8 to Q only where 8-J are red straight flushes. Then, there are the four straight situations; 89TJx, 9TJxK, and TJxKA. Then, of course, there are a great number of red flushes which will result in Queen wins, as well as all the red, on board, four flushes. As for all the other combinations, render them unto the Caesars. We'll have to be sharp to get this final number. But, we are calculating and thinking ad nauseum. Let's give way to the computer and the program written to solve these multi-hand probabilities.

COMPUTER RESULTS

A simulation of 500,000 hands was run and played to the end. The Kings won 405,144 hands, there were 1923 ties, and the Queens won 92,933 hands. The odds against the red Queens winning are 405,144:92,933= 4.4:1. The probability that the Queens will lose is 405,144/(500,000-1923)= 405,144/498,077= .81= 81%. Frank was right: Dave should have driven a harder bargain. In the annex, **THE POCKET PAIR**, the table states that if a pocket pair is taken to the river, at least a set will be made 19.2% of the time. That also means that 100-19.2= 80.8% of the time there will be no improvement. A rough guesstimate to the problem above, of Queens beating Kings, would be .192*.808= 15.5%, which is the probability of the Queens improving to at least a set while the Kings don't. Why is this figure lower than the simulated results? Because it does not take into account the other, fairly numerous ways in which Queens can win, such as participating in a greater number of straights.

SUMMARY

As we have seen, it is impractical to calculate multi-hand probabilities and come up with all the situations and numbers. The computer and program are king in this area, and, there are several books devoted to this subject available on the market. Nevertheless, the foundation of the game is the work contained in **this** book, and it is this material which makes this other work more intelligible. This ends the basic learning part of the book. From here, we move to the application of the techniques learned, and to doing a complete and systematic analysis of Hold'em probability.

PART II

Application

FOREWORD TO ANNEXES

The following annexes and appendices contain a detailed, comprehensive, and systematic treatment of Hold'em probabilities. Everything of importance is shown: the calculations, the thinking- the complete methodology needed to derive the probabilities. It will serve as your valuable and permanent **reference**, and tune-up your mind and your game when things are going bad.

The treatment is systematic in two respects: firstly, annexes and appendices cover the probabilities for all stages of the game from starting cards to the river, and secondly, other annexes and appendices cover all the categories of starting hands.

To cover the stages of the game, there are three annexes with tables: **HOLE CARDS**, which deals with starting hands, **THE FLOP**, which is a **generalized** look at the composition of the flop with several appendices, and, **TWO TO COME**, which covers all the situations from flop to river.

Everything begins with the starting hands, of which there are three main categories: pocket pairs, suited cards, and offsuit cards. With pocket pairs, we develop along the lines of sets and full houses; suited cards develop into the situations and numbers for flushes; for offsuit cards, we develop in the direction of a pair, two pairs, trips, and full houses. Then, we look at the sub-categories of connectors and suited connectors (one gap as well), and develop the situations and numbers for straights, and for straights and flushes in the case of suited connectors.

The annex, **HAND RANKINGS**, shows us

mathematically, why a straight flush beats quads, a flush beats a straight, a pair beats no pair, etc. The last annex, **TORONTO HOLD'EM**, is a humorous, but largely truthful, look at longshot poker in Toronto, and gives us an opportunity to look at a really tough, mind expanding, probability problem.

Peppered throughout this last part are discussions dealing with frequently asked questions or phenomena: the advantage of suited cards over offsuit cards, the running pair, why does two pair beat three pair?, and persistent improbability.

Finally, my poem, **A Gambler's Lament**, is a warning to those who would be more lucky than good.

HOLE CARDS

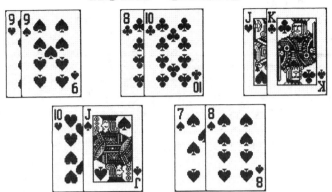

There are three general types of hole cards: **pairs**, **suited cards**, and **offsuit cards**, and a further two variants: **offsuit** and **onsuit connectors**. Each of these types hold varying possibilities, all of which we'll look at it in greater detail from flop to finish in later annexes.

POCKET PAIRS

With 52 cards, the total possible number of two card combinations is 52*51/2*1= 1326. The total number of different pairs which any rank (four cards) can make is 4*3/2*1= 6. Therefore, the total number of pairs which can be made from the 13 ranks is 13*6= 78. The probability of getting a pocket pair is 78/1326= .059= **5.9%**, and the odds against it are (1326-78):78= 1248:78= **16:1**.

SUITED CARDS

The number of two card suited combinations for any suit (13 cards) is 13*12/2*1= 78. The total number of suited combinations for all four suits is 4*78= 312, and the probability of getting suited cards is 312/1326= **23.5%**; odds against are **3.25:1**.

OFFSUIT CARDS

The number of offsuit **and** non-pair combinations, is the total number of combinations less the pairs and less the suited combinations, i.e., 1326-78-312= 936. The number of offsuit combinations can be verified by combining probabilities. Start with any card; the chances of the second card being of the same suit is 12/51 and the chances that the second card will make a pair is 3/51. Therefore, the probability that the second card will pair or make a suited combination is (12+3)/51= 15/51, so that the number of cards which will result in an offsuit combination is 51-15= 36. The number of offsuit combinations is 36/51*1326= 936; probability of **70.6%**.

SPECIFIC POCKET PAIR

The probability of getting any **specific** pair is 6/1326= 1/221= **.45%**, or odds against of **220:1**, while the probability of getting **any** pocket pair is 78/1326= 1/17= 5.88%, or odds against of 16:1.

POCKET As or Ks, or AK

The probability of getting pocket Aces, pocket Kings, or an AK, is the number of two card combinations which can be made from the four Aces and four Kings, over the total possible number of two card hands for 52 cards, i.e., 8*7/2*1/1326= 28/1326= **2.11%**, or odds against of (1326-28):28= 1298:28= **46.4:1**. The number of **AK** combinations is 8*7/2*1 minus the AA and KK combinations, i.e., 28-6-6= **16**. The probability of getting AK is 16/1326= **1.2%**, or odds against of 81.875:1= **82:1**. The odds against getting deuce 7, are likewise 82:1.

PREMIUM HANDS

By adding Queens to the Kings and Aces above, and thereby increasing the number of cards from eight to 12, the number of two card combinations possible, increases by more than two times. Most players consider a starting hand containing no card lower than a Queen to be a premium holding. The number of premium starting hands is 12*11/2*1= 132/2= **66**. The probability of getting this type of starting hand is 66/1326= .0498= .05= 5%. The breakdown of the premium hands: six pairs each of Aces, Kings, and Queens, and 16 combinations each of AK, AQ, and KQ (18+48= 66).

The odds against two players, heads-up, both having a specific pocket pair is also solved by combinations. One approach is to consider the two players as one, holding a four card combination of **xxxx**. The total possible number of four card combinations from a deck of 52 cards is 52*51*50*49/4*3*2*1= 270725. Only one of those combinations is **xxxx**, so that the probability of it happening is 1/270725.

OFFSUIT COMBINATIONS

The great mass of combinations are neither pairs, nor suited cards. There are 936 offsuit combinations ranging from deuce seven to TJ to AK. Let's dig deeper and find out more about those 936 combinations that we will be getting 936/1326= **70.6%** of the time.

CONNECTORS

Lay out cards of mixed suits, as shown on the next page, from A2....KA, for a total of 14 cards.

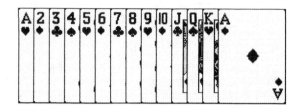

Observe that the number of two card
connectors is 13: A2, 23, 34,...KA. The
total number of A2 combinations is the
number of ways in which the As and 2s can be
taken in two ways minus the AA and 22
combinations, i.e., 8*7/2*1-(6+6)= 28-12=
16. There are 16 A2 combinations, four of
which are suited, and 12 which are offsuit.
For the entire deck, the total number of
suited and offsuit connectors is 13*16= **208**;
the total number of offsuit connectors is
13*12= 156 and the total number of suited
connectors is 13*4= 52. But not all
connectors have similar potential. With A2,
you can flop only one straight. With TJ, you
can flop four different straights because it
has maximum stretch, i.e., three ranks
below, and three ranks above the connector.
Seven connector combinations have this
characteristic: 45, 56, 67, 78, 89, 9T, and
TJ. The total number of suited and offsuit
connectors offering maximum stretch is 7*16=
112. With 34 and QJ, the number of straights
which each can flop is three; for 23 and KQ,
the number of straights which each can flop
is two; for A2 and KA, the number of
straights which each can flop is one. Of
course, with JQ, QK, and KA, we have high
pair and high flush potential as well. Among
the offsuit combinations are hands like AQ

and KJ all the way down to deuce and 7, really quite a spectrum. Some of those combinations are offsuit and playable, while others are definitely "unsuited" as playing hands.

PLAYABLE HANDS

Finally, if you were a fairly disciplined player, but not so disciplined as to play only premium hands as defined and determined previously, and only played pairs and hands where your lowest card was a Ten, the number of hands you could play, would be all the two card combinations for 20 cards (Ts,Js, Qs, Ks, and As), plus all the pairs from deuces to 9s (eight ranks). That number would be 20*19/2*1 + 8*6= 190+48= **238**. The probability that your hand will meet this criteria is 238/1326= .179= **18%**. If you further tightened your starting requirements by dropping the pairs, deuces to 6s, the number of hands you could be playing would be 190+18= **208**. The probability that your starting hand will meet this criteria is 208/1326= **15.7%**. Now, that still gives you a lot of opportunities to play cards.

Note:
In all the tables which follow the annexes, the probability and odds numbers are rounded off to intelligible and rememberable numbers, and because of this, these numbers may differ **slightly** from those in other books. **No problem.** By including the number of **combinations** for each situation, the **exact** numbers can always be calculated.

TABLE OF STARTING HANDS

	# of combos*	%	Odds
A pocket pair	78	5.9	16:1
Suited cards	312	23.5	3.25:1
Offsuit cards, non-pairs	936	70.6	.4:1
Total # of combos	1326		
Pocket Aces	6	.45	220:1
JJ to KK	18	1.4	73:1
66 to TT	30	2.3	43:1
22 to 55	24	1.8	54:1
AA, KK, or AK	28	2.1	46:1
All AKs	16	1.2	82:1
AK suited	4	.3	331:1
AK offsuit	12	.9	110:1
Deuce 7	16	1.2	82:1
Suited connectors max stretch	28	2.1	46:1
Offsuit connectors max stretch	84	6.3	15:1
All max stretch connectors	112	8.5	11:1
Premium starting hands**	66	5	19:1
A pair, and two cards T and above	244	18	4.4:1
Pairs 7 and up, cards T and above	208	16	5.4:1

* of total possible number of 1326
** all pocket As, Ks, and Qs, plus all AKs, AQs, and KQs.

Note:
The number of pair combinations for Aces is six. The number of AK combinations is 16. The likelihood of a raiser having AK as opposed to AA (assumes that this player raises with both those types of hands) is 16/6= 2 2/3 times.

THE FLOP

The flop defines your hand, and in doing so, elicits emotional responses ranging from disgust and bitter disappointment, to elation, to cat killing curiosity, to overwhelming optimism, to cautious optimism, to hope, to confusion, to a sinking feeling, to feeling foolish, to feeling bored, to feeling cursed, to name a few. For anyone less than devout, it can shake or make your belief in God. With the flop, you see 3/7= **43%** of your hand, whereas before the flop, you have 2/7= 29% of your hand.

Let's look at a typical Toronto poker scenario: a man with pocket deuces calls in first position and is raised by a woman with AQ of diamonds in the next position; a man with red pocket Kings reraises; a fellow with black AK offsuit reluctantly calls because he knows the two raisers are good players, but, these are the best cards he has seen in a long time; a man with red pocket 10s calls three bets cold, reasoning that with this many callers it's worth it; a rock with pocket Jacks on the button folds; a player with JT of spades in the small blind reasons she's got a chance to win and calls two and one-half bets; that luck-oriented fellow with 6 and 7 of hearts in the big blind figures he's a cinch since all the high cards are out, and reraises; the fellow with pocket deuces, remembering the refrain, "deuces never loses", caps it. So much confidence, so much hope.

After a flop of deuce, 8 and 9 of hearts, the situation looks and goes like this:

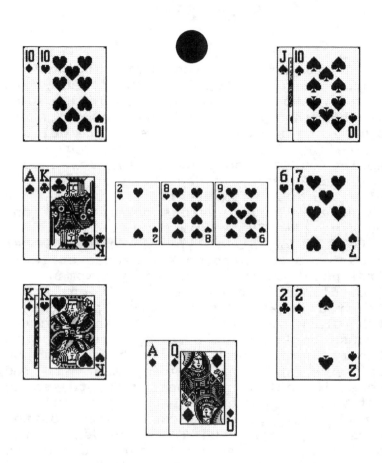

the JT of spades checks; there is a bet and
the set of deuces follows with a raise; the
lady with AQ of diamonds feels disgust and
fires her cards at the dealer; the fellow
with red pocket Kings feels a certain
guarded elation and just calls; the formerly

88

reluctant caller with black AK offsuit feels real foolish and folds; the man with the Ts is curious to see what his overpair and Ten high flush draw will bring and wants to pull off another card no matter what, so he calls; the JT of spades, who checked the flop, feels confusion about whether to go for a straight in face of a flush possibly made or certain flush draws, but calls just in case; the 6 and 7 of hearts is overwhelmingly optimistic and raises; the determined deuces cap; the Kings call; the Tens call; the JT gets the message and now folds. The probability of these individual events is contained in later annexes. Who wins? The pocket deuces of course: the turn is a Ten of diamonds, the river is the case deuce, and the pot is huge. This example does show that although individual probabilities for weaker hands may be low, weaker hands taken collectively pack quite a punch.

That was a specific look at the flop. In the next few paragraphs, I'd like to look at the flop in a more general way, much like **the objective observer** would. The observer would see some flops containing three of one suit, some of three different suits, some with three cards in sequence, some with a pair, etc. Let us take a systematic and probabilistic look at the flop.

For this situation, we are not involved in a hand, therefore, there are 52 cards available from which to draw upon for a flop. The total possible number of three cards flops from 52 cards is $52*51*50/3*2*1 = 132600/6 = 22100$. This becomes our reference combination. Our approach will be systematic by looking at flops containing the following: trips, pairs, and no pairs; three, two and no suits; three, two, and no sequences; and cards above and below the median rank of 8. By the end, we'll have a greater understanding of why the flop comes as it does. For all the probabilities of improving specific starting hands see the annexes, **THE POCKET PAIR, OFFSUIT CARDS, SUITED CARDS, CONNECTORS,** and **SUITED CONNECTORS.**

TRIPS, PAIRS, AND NO PAIRS

Trips. The number of trips, or three of a kind, which any rank can make is 4*3*2/3*2*1= 24/6= 4. The number of trips for 13 ranks is 13*4= 52. The probability of seeing trips on the flop is 52/22100= .235= .24%.

Pairs. The number of pairs which any rank can make is 4*3/2*1= 6. The number of different pairs for 13 ranks is 13*6= 78. Any pair can have as the third card of the flop, any of the other 48 cards. Therefore, the number of flops containing a pair is 78*48= 3744. The probability that the flop will contain a pair is 3744/22100= .169= **16.9%**, a rather frequent occurrence.

No Pairs. The number of flops which do not contain trips or a pair, i.e., three different ranks, are 22100 minus the trips and pair flops, or 22100-52-3744= 18304. The probability that the flop will contain three different ranks is 18304/22100= .828= **82.8%**. To verify by combining probabilities start with any card; the probability that the next card will not be a pair is (51-3)/51= 48/51, and the probability that the third card will not pair the first or second card is (50-3-3)/50= 44/50. The probability that the flop

will contain no pair or three of a kind is
48/51*44/50= .828= **82.8%**.

SUITS

Three Suits. The total possible number of
three card suited combinations which any
suit can make is 13*12*11/3*2*1= 1716/6=
286. The four suits can make a total of
4*286= 1144 same suit combinations. The
probability that the flop will come suited
is 1144/22100= .052= **5.2%**.

Two Suits. The total possible number of
two card suited combinations which any suit
can make is 13*12/2*1= 156/2= 78. Any of
those 78 combinations can have as its third
card, any of the 52-13= 39 other different
suit cards, giving 78*39= 3042 two suit
combinations, some of which will contain a
pair on board. The same is true for the
other suits, giving a total of 4*3042= 12168
two suit flops. The probability that the
flop will contain two suited cards is
12168/22100= .55= **55%**. Now you see why
someone always seems to be on a flush draw.

Three Different Suits. The total possible
number of three different suit flops is the
total number of flops minus the sum of the
three suit and two suit flops, i.e., 22100-
1144-12168= 8788. The probability that the
flop will come with three different suits is
8788/22100= .398= **39.8%**. To verify by
combining probabilities, start with any
card. The probability that the second card
will not be of the same suit is (51-12)/51=
39/51, and the probability that the third
card will not be of the same suit as the
previous two is (50-12-12)/50= 26/50. The
probability of three different suits is
39/51*26/50= .3976= **39.8%**.

91

SEQUENCES

Lay out the 13 ranks from left to right in order, and include the A on the left as well- A23456789TJQKA. The lowest three card sequence is A23, then 234, ... etc. In total, there are 12, three card sequences. Looking again, but this time at two card sequences, we see that there is a total of 13 two card sequences. How probable is it that the flop will come three or two sequenced? We shall see in the paragraphs below.

Three Sequenced. In the chapter, **REFERENCE COMBINATIONS**, we looked at the 7s, 8s, and 9s, to determine how many three card combinations could be made which contained neither trips or a pair, i.e., 789 in any order. That number was 64. The same will be true for any other group of three ranks. Therefore, the number of three card sequence combinations is 12*64= 768. The probability that the flop will come with three cards in sequence (any order) is 768/22100= .035= 3.5%.

Two Sequenced. For two card sequences, let us look at the 5s and 6s, and determine the number of 5 and 6 combinations. The total possible number of two card combinations from the four 5s and four 6s is 8*7/2*1= 56/2= 28. The 55 and 66 pair combinations, six of each, must be stripped out. The number of 5 and 6 combinations is 28-6-6= 16, just as it was for AK. Any of those sixteen 5 and 6 combinations may have as its third card......hold on! To be only a two card sequence, the third card cannot be any of the 4s or 7s, leaving 50-8= 42 cards as the third member. The number of flops containing 56x, where x is not a 4 or 7, but any other rank including a 5 or 6, is 16*42= 672. But the A2 and KA combinations do not have a rank below or a rank above respectively. For those two, the number of cards which may be the third card is 50-4= 46. The number of two sequence flop combinations for either the A2 or KA combinations is 16*46= 736. The total possible number of two sequence flops is 2*736 + 11*672= 1472+7392= 8864. The probability that the flop will contain two cards in sequence is 8864/22100= .40= **40%**, a rather frequent occurrence that helps to explain why it appears someone is always on a straight draw.

No Sequenced. The probability that the flop will contain no cards in sequence is the total number of flops minus the sum of the three and two sequenced flops, i.e., (22100-768-8864)/22100= 12468/22100= **56.4%**. Note that this cannot be done by combining probabilities because of the fact that the A2 and KA combinations have more two sequence possibilities than the other two card combinations.

CARDS ABOVE

For the situations in which we hold a pocket pair, we'd like to know the probability of cards higher than our pair appearing on the flop. The answer is obvious for the Ace and the deuce so I will not deal with them, except to say that the flop could come 222, and in that improbable case, you have nothing to worry about. Unlike the cases above, where we used 52 cards, here we will use 48 cards (the deck minus the four of our rank). Therefore, we are not including any of those flops which would give us a set or quads. Also, we will not make any assumptions about other players' hands- whether someone has an Ace or King when we hold pocket Queens. Therefore, we are looking at whether the flop will throw up a red flag, i.e., a card higher than our pocket pair.

For the median pair of pocket 8s, there are six ranks above (24 cards) and six ranks below (24 cards). To determine the probability of the flop containing one or more cards above an 8, we first need to determine the total possible number of flops with 48 cards, and then determine the number of flops which the deuces to 7s can make. With those numbers we can manipulate and solve.

The total possible number of flops with 48 cards is 48*47*46/3*2*1= 103776/6= 17296. With the 24 cards which rank below the 8s, the total possible number of three card combinations is 24*23*22/3*2*1= 12144/6= 2024. By deduction, every other combination contains one or more cards higher than an 8. Therefore, that number of combinations is 17296-2024= 15272. The probability that one or more cards higher than an 8 will be on the flop is 15272/17296= .883= **88.3%**. Verifying by combining probabilities: the probability that the first cards will not be above an 8 is 24/48, and the probabilities for the second and third card are 23/47 and 22/46. The combined probability is 24/48*23/47*22/46= .117= 11.7%. The probability that the flop will contain a card above 8 is 100-11.7= **88.3%**. Note that if you tried to use the same probabilities and apply them to cards above an 8, you'd end up with the number of flops which contained all cards above an 8. And once again by shotgunning; there is a 50% chance that the first card will not be above an 8, same for the second, and same for the third. That makes a .5*.5*.5= .125= 12.5% probability of no card higher than an 8. The probability of a card higher than an 8 is 100-12.5= 87.5%.

For any rank, the general formula is to calculate the number of three card combinations which the ranks below can make, and subtract that from the reference number of 17296, manipulate and solve. One more example with pocket Queens- the number of ranks below is 10, giving 40 cards. The total possible number of three card combinations from 40 cards is 40*39*38/3*2*1= 9880. The number of combinations which will contain one or more cards above a Queen is 17296-9880= 7416. The probability that the flop will contain a card or cards higher than a Queen is 7416/17296= .429= **42.9%**. Of course, these numbers will be lower if you want to make assumptions about what other players are holding. In that case, you will have to make adjustments as in the next section.

ACE APPEARANCES

Finally, as the joke goes, the first rule of pocket Kings is that an Ace will flop. If one opponent holds an Ace, say AQ, then there are three Aces remaining. What is the probability that a single Ace and no King will be on the flop? With 48 cards remaining, the total possible number of three card flops is 48*47*46/3*2*1= 103776/6= 17296. The single Ace model is

Axy, where xy is any two cards except an Ace or King. That leaves (52-4-4= 44 cards, less one Queen) 43 cards. The number of xy combinations is 43*42/2*1= 1806/2= 903. Any of those xy combinations can combine with either of the three remaining Aces giving 3*903= 2709 flops containing an Ace. The probability that the flop will contain a single Ace under the conditions described is 2709/17296= .157= 15.7%.

If two opponents hold an A with some other card which is not a King, the number of cards available for the flop is 52-6= 46. The total possible number of flops is 46*45*44/3*2*1= 15180. The number of cards available for xy, in the model Axy, where x and y are neither Kings nor Aces is 42 (52 less four As, less four Ks, less the other two cards held by the Ace holders) and the number of xy combinations is 42*41/2*1= 861. The probability of the flop containing a single Ace and no Kings is 2*861/15180= 1722/15180= .113= 11.3%.

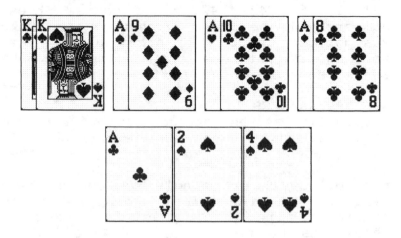

When you're really going bad, we have the situation as depicted on the previous page. Your three opponents holding an A and other card except a King, manage to somehow scare up that last Ace. The number of cards available for the flop is 52-8= 44. The total possible number of flops for this situation is 44*43*42/3*2*1= 13244. The number of cards available for xy, in the model Axy, where x and y are neither Kings nor Aces is 41 (52 less four As, less four Ks, less the other three cards held by the Ace holders) and the number of xy combinations is 41*40/2*1= 820. The probability of the flop containing that remaining Ace is 820/13244= .062= 6.2%.

Then there's **real freeze/unease.** You have three opponents, neither of whom holds an Ace nor a King. You hold pocket Kings. What is the probability of an Ace and no King coming up? The total possible number of flops for 44 cards is 13244. The model for an Ace on the flop is Axy, where xy is any of the two card combinations which can be made from 38 cards (52 minus four Aces minus four Kings minus their six cards, whatever they are). The number of two card combinations is 38*37/2*1= 703. Either of the four Aces can combine with either of the 703 combinations. The probability of an Ace and no King coming up on the flop is 4*703/17296= 2812/13244= .212= **21%**.

Finally, if Kings can have this much trouble with an overcard, it's easy to understand why smaller pocket pairs usually have flops with overcards, and that it most often requires a set to take the pot. All the preceding material is tabulated in the following appendices.

GENERAL FLOP TABLE

For 52 cards and 22100 flops,
the probability that
the flop will contain:

	# combos	%	Odds
TRIPS, PAIRS, NO PAIRS			
Trips (three of a kind)	52	.24	424:1
A pair	3744	17	5:1
No pair	18304	83	.2:1
SUITS			
Three of same suit	1144	5	18:1
Two of same suit	12168	55	.8:1
Three different suits	8788	40	1.5:1
SEQUENCES			
Three in sequence	768	3.5	28:1
Two in sequence	8864	40	1.5:1
No sequence	12468	56.4	.8:1

CARDS ABOVE

The probability that a
higher card will flop*
when you hold pocket:

	# combos below	# combos above	%	Odds**
Kings	13244	4052	23	3.3:1
Queens	9880	7416	43	1.3:1
Jacks	7140	10156	59	.7:1
Tens	4960	12336	71	.3:1
9s	3276	14020	81	.2:1
8s	2024	15272	88	.1:1
7s	1140	16156	93	.07:1
6s	560	16736	97	.03:1
5s	220	17076	99	.01:1
4s	56	17240	99.7	.003:1
3s	4	17292	99.9	.0002:1

* for 48 cards and a possible 17296 flops. Assumes four of the higher cards
are available and excludes the possibilty of you getting a set or quads.
** odds against a higher card than the pocket pair on the flop

Comments:

   With pocket Jacks and lower, the probability that a higher card will
flop rapidly increases, and in practice, you often need to make a set to
win the hand. For the probability of making a set, see the annex, **THE
POCKET PAIR.** The above situations are, however, a bit artificial in this
respect; it assumes that all four cards of the ranks above yours are
available for the flop. A more realistic situation is shown in the next
table, where we take into account the holdings of your opponents.

But, let's do one example to illustrate the approach- pocket Qs against AQ
and KQ. The number of three card combinations for the flop is
46*45*44/3*2*1= 15180. For the models Axy and Kxy, xy is any two card
combination from the remaining 40 cards (52 minus all the As, Ks, and Qs).
The number of xy combinations is 40*39/2*1= 780. Any of the three remaining
As or Ks may combine with either of the 780 combinations. The probability
of an A or K on the flop is 6*780/15180= 30.8= 31%.

TABLE OF ACE APPEARANCES

You are holding pocket Kings, if

	%
one opponent holds an Ace*, another A will flop	15.7
two opponents hold an Ace*, another A will flop	11.3
three opponents hold an Ace*, another A will flop	6.2
neither of your three opponents holds an Ace*, an Ace will flop	21

* and no King(s)

TWO TO COME

After the flop, you have seen five of seven cards, or 5/7= 71% of your hand. Deciding correctly on whether to remain involved or to pass, is probably the difference between being a lifelong winner or loser, if, you are fairly correct in your starting requirements for the game you are in, position, etc. Knowing the odds and comparing them to the pot odds and implied odds is crucial, as well as the ability to put your opponents on probable hands, and **adjust your probability of winning**, accordingly. Your straight draw against her flush draw heads-up, is probably a pass situation (your **maximum** six outs at best [only three outs below], against her nine outs) if you have nothing else going for you.

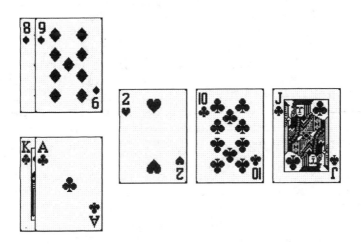

The probabilities for completing your hand from flop to river, (47 unseen cards and two to come), flop to turn (47 unseen cards), and turn to river, (46 unseen cards), are given in the tables for situations in which the number of outs is known. For, flop to river (**two to come**), the probabilities are further broken down to show the chances of hitting one of your outs, hitting two of your outs, and hitting one **or** two of your outs. For example, in the case for 21 outs, the probability of hitting only one of your outs is 51%, the probability of hitting two of your outs is 19%, and the probability of hitting one or two of your outs is 51+19= 70%. This was done, because in many situations, hitting two of your outs will cause you to lose the pot, or conversely, make you more money when someone makes trips to your straight. If you have a three flush after the flop, you may want to know the odds against hitting two running suits, i.e., hitting two of your 10 outs. If you have flopped a weak flush, any of the remaining flush cards become **"douts"** (see paragraph below). Each situation needs to be fully broken down, because within the same situation, a pair is disastrous, but making a seven card straight might not be, and then again, it might be. Poker is a game of shifting odds, and requires the winning player to think and deduce, again and again.

I have come up with the word, **"douts"**, pronounced like "doubts", to express the reverse concept of outs. Douts can destroy hands which are made, or largely made on the flop, such as low end straights, small flushes, two small pairs, or a less than nut flush made on the turn. A mathematical awareness of douts can temper a tendency to overpush a small advantage when you have a lot of players breathing down your neck, and end up saving you a lot of money.

The combinations method was used for determining probabilities, except for the column, SG (Shotgun). Combinations allow us to break down the probabilities into hitting one out only, hitting two outs, as well as hitting one or two outs. For the probability of hitting one or two of your outs, we can also use combined probabilities by the missing method. The following example is representative of how the figures were arrived at.

After the flop, there are 47 remaining cards. The total possible number of two card combinations is 47*46/2*1= 1081. For the case of 9 outs, either one out can fall and a blank or vice versa, or, two outs can fall. For the case of two outs falling, the number of two card out combinations which can be made from 9 cards is 9*8/2*1= 72/2= 36. For the case of one falling, the number of blanks is 47-9= 38. Either of the 9 outs can combine with either of the 38 blanks, giving us 9*38= 342 combinations. Now, we can solve. The probability of hitting two of your outs is 36/1081= 3.3= 3%. The probability of hitting only one of your outs is 342/1081= 31.6= 32%. The probability of hitting either one or two of your outs is 3+32= 35%. The number of combinations for both possibilities, and hitting one or two outs are included in the first table as a permanent reference. Now, the solution by combining probabilities: the chances of missing an out on the turn are (47-9)/47= 38/47. If we miss, then the chances of missing an out on the river are (46-9)/46= 37/46. The combined probability of missing an out is 38/47*37/46= 1406/2162= 65%. The probability of hitting one or two outs is 100-65= 35%. Voila.

For the **SG** (shotgun) column, the probability is arrived at using the following reasoning: I have 9 outs and two chances to get one or two of my outs, therefore, I have 18 shots out of 47, or, a probability of 18/47= 38% to make my hand. That's close, and close counts in grenades, horseshoes, and more often than not, in poker. I have enclosed the **SG** probabilities in brackets where the error is greater than 3%.

Some quick observations about the table: the greater the number of outs, the greater the probability that you will hit two of your outs, which can be the downside of having too many outs, and, shotgunning for 10 outs and below gets you pretty close.

Following the first probability table is a discussion on the running pair, followed by another appendix listing some hands ordered by the number of outs and douts, and another appendix listing turn and river probabilities.

TABLE OF TWO TO COME

Probability and odds to:

O U T S	hit ONE only %	#combos	to hit TWO %	#combos	TO HIT ONE or TWO %	#combos	Odds	SG %	Odds
21	50.5	546	19.4	210	69.9	756	.43:1	(89)	
20	50	540	17.6	190	67.5	730	.48:1	(85)	
19	49.2	532	15.8	171	65	703	.54:1	(81)	
18	48.3	522	14.2	153	62.4	675	.60:1	(77)	
17	47.2	510	12.6	136	59.8	646	.67:1	(72)	
16	45.9	496	11.1	120	57	616	.75:1	(68)	
15	44.4	480	9.7	105	54.1	595	.85:1	(64)	
14	42.7	462	8.4	91	51.2	553	.95:1	(60)	
13	40.9	442	7.2	78	48.1	520	1.1:1	(55)	
12	38.9	420	6.1	66	45	486	1.2:1	(51)	
11	36.6	396	5.1	55	41.7	451	1.4:1	(47)	
10	34.2	370	4.2	45	38.4	415	1.6:1	(43)	
9	31.6	342	3.3	36	35	378	1.9:1	38	1.6:1
8	28.9	312	2.6	28	31.5	340	2.2:1	34	1.9:1
7	25.9	280	1.9	21	27.8	301	2.6:1	30	2.4:1
6	22.8	246	1.4	15	24.1	261	3.2:1	26	2.9:1
5	19.4	210	.9	10	20.4	220	3.9:1	21	3.7:1
4	15.9	172	.6	6	16.5	178	5:1	17	4.9:1
3	12.2	132	.3	3	12.5	135	7:1	13	6.8:1
2	8.3	90	.1	1	8.4	91	11:1	8.5	11:1
1	4.3	46	0	0	4.3	46	22:1	4.3	23:1

Also see Discussion next page.

DISCUSSION

Often hands are won or lost by a running pair on the last two cards. The next pages depict and quantify four situations.

Situation 1. The set of 7s, losing after the flop to a straight already made, improves to a full house with a running pair of 3s to beat the straight.

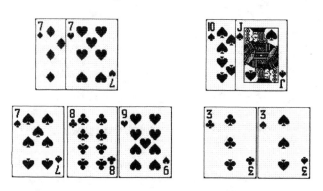

The probability of a running pair for the cases of a **set** or **trips** on the flop is determined as follows: there are 10 ranks which have not made an appearance as far as the holder of the set or trips is concerned. Each of those 10 ranks can be combined into six pairs. Therefore, there are 10*6= 60 possible running pairs. After the flop, there are 47 cards remaining. The total possible number of two card combinations which can be made from 47 cards is 47*46/2*1= 1081. Therefore, the probability of hitting a running pair is 60/1081= 5.6%. With two cards to come, the full house or quads may also be made with the seven outs which have a probability of 27.8%, **plus** the additional probability of a running pair, for a **total probability** of 27.8+5.6= **33.4%**

Situation 2. The running pair also plays in the case of top pair against two lower pair as depicted below.

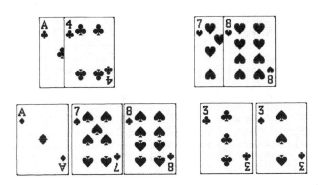

The number of outs for the holder of the top pair is his two remaining high cards, plus his three kicker cards, i.e., 5 cards and a probability of 20.4% to improve, as well as a running pair from the remaining nine ranks. The number of different pairs from nine ranks is 9*6=54. This adds an increased probability of 54/1081= 4.99= 5%. The probability that top pair will beat the two lower pair (if the two lower pair do not improve) is 20.4+5= 25.4%.

Situation 3. The running pair also comes in to play where two players both flop top pair, but the player with the lower kicker also pairs up, as depicted on the next page. The player with AJ has top pair and a good kicker. The other player has made As and 5s, i.e., two pair. The player with AJ can improve by hitting one of his six outs (the three Jacks or the three 6s, or he can hit an unrelated running pair above the rank of 6 (7s, 8s, 9s, Ts, Qs, Ks). The

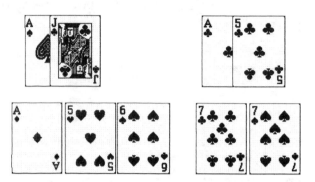

probability of the player with AJ beating
the player with Aces up is 24.1% (from the
six outs), plus the probability of hitting
a running pair. The probability of hitting
a running pair from the six available ranks
is 6*6/1081= 36/1081= 3.3%. The total
probability is 24.1+3.3= 27.4%.

Situation 4. Here AJ has flopped the top two
pair. The A8 can win, only with running 8s.
The probability of hitting two of his three
outs is .3% (**Table of Two To Come**). A8 can
also tie with running 4s, Qs or Ks.

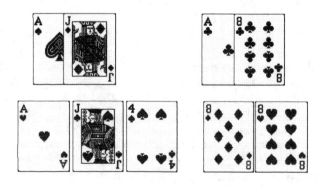

OUTS AND DOUTS

21 outs: for a flush and straight draw with two overcards (9+6+6)

20

19

18 outs: for a flush draw with two overcards and an inside straight draw (9+6+3), e.g., you hold AcKc, and the flop comes JcTh2c.

17

16

15 outs: for a straight and flush draw (6+9); for a flush draw with two overcards (9+6)

15 douts: you have top pair, but believe there are a straight and flush draw against you

14 outs: for an open-ended straight draw with two overcards (8+4)

13 outs: for two pair and a flush draw with one card to come (4+9) 12 outs: for a flush draw with one overcard (9+3)

11 outs: for an open-ended straight draw with one overcard, e.g., you hold Q9 and the flop comes JT2

10 outs: for a set or trips to a full house or quads with one card to come; with two to come, for an open-ended straight draw with two overcards but where an opponent flopped a four flush (6+4); for backdooring a flush you must hit two of your outs; for an open-ended straight draw with a pair where trips will also win,

9 outs: for a flush draw

9 douts: for your open-ended straight draw against a flush draw

8 outs: for an open-ended straight draw; for a belly buster straight draw

8 douts: when you have flopped a weak flush, or turned a weak flush, and do not want to see any more of your suit,

7 outs: for trips or a set on the flop to improve to a full house or quads with two cards to come**; to make a full house or quads on the turn after making a set or trips on the flop; you have flopped a nut flush while another player holds a high suited card and you want him to make a losing flush

7 douts: you have flopped a straight with your two cards making the idiot end, e.g., 78 and the flop is 9TJ, and your opponent holds Qx so that the three remaining 8s and the four Ks make a higher straight; you've made a less than nut flush on the turn and suspect that someone holds a higher flush card, so that another flush card will kill your hand

6 outs: for an an open-ended straight draw where an opponent has flopped a four flush; for your one pair and inside straight draw where improving to trips or the straight makes a win; the flop is low and ragged and you have two overcards; for your top pair with a good kicker against an opponent holding the same pair who paired his kicker where the third card is higher than low kicker, so that your outs are your three kicker cards, and the three cards which pair the other card, plus a running pair***

5 outs: for a nut or better flush draw when you hold KcQh and the flop comes Ac9c3c and two other players have flopped a flush

5 douts: for your holding 56 suited against AK when the flop comes A56, any A (two remaining) or any K (three remaining) or any running pair from the remaining nine ranks (9*6=54, 54/1081= 4.99= 5%)

4 outs: for two pair to full house; for an

inside straight draw

3 outs: to make top pair when holding an overcard to the flop; top pair, small kicker, needs his kicker running pair to beat top two pair on the flop

2 outs: to make a set or quads while holding a pocket pair and you have missed the flop; for an open-ended straight flush draw against a stronger hand

1 out: to make a set when one of your cards is flashed; for an inside straight flush draw; when the flop comes three of a kind and the fourth comes to make your Ace a winning hand; for your lower set to beat a higher set

1 dout: your higher set to lose to a lower set

** the full house is also made with an unrelated running pair from any of the other ten ranks (six different pairs for each rank). The probability of doing so is 10*6/1081= 60/1081= 5.6%. That figure is added to 27.8 giving a total probability of 33.4%. Also see note #1 in previous section.
*** the running pair must be higher than the kicker which was paired on the flop. To determine the probability, determine the number of ranks above that kicker which have not made an appearance, multiply by six and divide by 1081. See situation 3 in previous section.

O U T S	Turn Prob *(x/47)	^Odds (47-x)/x:1	TURN AND RIVER River Prob (x/46)	Odds (46-x)/x:1
	%		%	
21	45	1.2:1	46	1.2:1
20	43	1.3:1	44	1.3:1
19	40	1.5:1	41	1.4:1
18	38	1.6:1	39	1.6:1
17	36	1.8:1	37	1.7:1
16	34	1.9:1	35	1.9:1
15	32	2.1:1	33	2.1:1
14	30	2.4:1	30	2.3:1
13	28	2.6:1	28	2.5:1
12	26	2.9:1	26	2.8:1
11	23	3.3:1	24	3.2:1
10	21	3.7:1	22	3.6:1
9	19	4.2:1	20	4.1:1
8	17	4.9:1	17	4.8:1
7	15	5.7:1	15	5.7:1
6	13	6.8:1	13	6.7:1
5	11	8.4:1	11	8.2:1
4	9	11:1	9	11:1
3	6	15:1	7	14:1
2	4	23:1	4	22:1
1	2	46:1	2	45:1

^ the odds against hitting one of your outs
* x equals the number of outs

THE POCKET PAIR

One in every 17 hands that are dealt to you should be a pocket pair. If not, then you are having an improbable session. The odds of improving to at least a set on the flop are 7.51:1. Most often, in order to conserve your bankroll, you'll have to employ a policy of catch and release with the smaller pairs. When you do make a set, you'll have a well-disguised hand and need to employ good strategy and tactics to reel in and land a trophy pot. But that is beyond the scope of this book, so let's work out all the odds and all the situations that can develop from a pocket pair.

BEFORE THE FLOP

Before the flop, the total possible number of two card hands is 52*51/2*1= 1326. Each rank can make 4*3/2*1= 6 pair combinations. The total number of different pair combinations is 6*13= 78. The probability of getting a pocket pair is 78/1326= 1/17, or odds against of 16:1. The probability of getting a specific pair is 6/1326, or 1/221, or odds against of 220:1.

FLOPPING QUADS

The numbers with respect to the flop: with your pocket pair, say 8s, there are 50 unseen cards. The total possible number of three card combinations (flops), with 50 cards is $50*49*48/3*2*1= 19600$. Nothing can excite like seeing quads on the flop and bring out the tactician and strategist in you. Quad 8s are represented by the model 88x, where x is any of the remaining 48 cards. The number of 88x combinations is 48, and the probability of flopping quad 8s is $48/19600= .25\%$, or odds against of $(19600-48):48= 407:1$.

FLOPPING A SET

The probability of flopping a set is represented by the model 8xy, where x and y represents any two card combination which is not a pair from the remaining 48 cards. Unlike trips, only one player can have a set. The total possible number of two card combinations which can be made from 48 cards is $48*47/2*1= 1128$. A certain number of those combinations are pairs which must be subtracted from the 1128 two card combinations. The number of pairs possible from the 12 remaining ranks is $12*6= 72$. The number of two card combinations not containing a pair is $1128-72= 1056$. Each of those 1056 combinations may combine with either of the remaining two 8s, giving $2*1056= 2112$ 8xy combinations. The probability of hitting a set on the flop is $2112/19600= .108= 10.8\%$. The odds against hitting a set are $(19600-2112):2112= 8.3:1$.

FLOPPING A FULL HOUSE

The probability of flopping a full house

is represented by the model 8yy, where yy is any pair. As determined in the paragraph above, the number of pairs is 72. Since each of the pair combinations may combine with either of the remaining 8s, there are 2*72= 144 combinations making 8s full. The probability of flopping a full house is 144/19600= .735= .74%, or odds against of (19600-144):144= 136:1.

FLOPPING AT LEAST A SET
The probability of flopping either quads, a set, or a full house (also expressed as "at least a set") is (48+2112+144)/19600= 2304/19600= .118= 11.8%, or odds against of (19600-2304):2304= 7.51:1.

The **overall** probability of 11.8%, can also be calculated by combining the probabilities of not hitting an 8. With 50 cards remaining, the probability of not hitting an 8 with the first card is 48/50. If we miss, the probability of not hitting an 8 with the second card is 47/49, and for the third card, it is 46/48. Combining the probabilities, we have 48/50*47/49*46/48= 103776/117600= 88.2%. The probability of hitting at least a set is 100-88.2= 11.8%. The odds against it are (117600-(117600-103776)):117600-103776= (117600-13824):13824= 7.51:1. Combining probabilities is a simple method for arriving at the big picture.

The shotgun type says, I've got two outs with three cards coming. That gives me six shots out of 50, or 6/50= 12%, or odds against of (50-6):6= 44:6= 7.3:1, which is pretty close.

BEYOND THE FLOP FOR A FULL HOUSE OR QUADS

In this situation, we'll look at the case where we make a set on the flop and want to know the probability of improving to quads or a full house, with two cards to come. We could use, **TABLE OF TWO TO COME**, with seven outs, but this would initially give us an incorrect answer, because we can also make a full house by getting an unrelated running pair, as we'll see later.

The flop model for the set is 8xy, where x and y are any two cards except a pair. With two cards to come and 47 remaining, there are $47*46/2*1=$ 1081 two card combinations. The one remaining 8 may combine with any of the other 46 cards giving 46 quad making combinations. A full house will be made in the following situations: if either one x or y drops, if two Xs or two Ys drop, if x and y drop, or we get a different running pair. Take the xy, xx, or yy situations first; there are three Xs and three Ys remaining. The number of two card combinations making a full house of the type xx, yy, and xy, which the six cards can make is $6*5/2*1=$ 30/2= 15, done. Now either x alone, or y alone, can combine with any of the remaining 40 cards (47 less the one 8, less the three Xs, less the three Ys). That gives $6*40=$ 240 combinations. Finally, any pair from the remaining 40 cards (10 ranks) will also make a full house. The number of these pair combinations is $10*6=$ 60. The total number of combinations which make at least a full house is 46+15+240+60= 361. The probability of making at least a full house with two cards to come is 361/1081= .3339= **33.4%**. The odds against doing so are (1081-361):361= 1.99:1= 2:1. Note that when the xx or yy combinations fall, you could make an unfavourable full house, as well as losing to someone else's quads. Those are judgement calls.

We can also use, **TABLE OF TWO TO COME**, with a minor modification. With seven outs, we get a probability of 27.8%, which covers all the ways in which to make a full house or quads, except for an unrelated running pair. The probability of hitting a running pair is 60/1081= 5.6%. Adding the two probabilities together, we have 27.8+5.6= 33.4%, a much quicker solution.

By shotgunning, we have one 8, and six Xs and Ys in total, giving 7 outs. With two cards to come, we have 14 shots out of 47, or 14/47= 29.8%. This time we undershoot with shotgunning.

For the turn, we simply have seven outs. Looking at the table, **TURN AND RIVER**, we have a probability of 7/47= 14.89= **15%**.

With one card to come, we have picked up three additional outs from the turn card and there are now 10 outs. The probability of making quads or a full house on the river is 10/46= .2174= 21.7= **22%**, or odds against of (46-10):10= **3.6:1**.

NO FOLD'EM HOLD'EM

What about if the pot is so huge before the flop, or you're all in, so that it's to the river regardless. What are your chances of improving to a set, full house, or even quads?

The best way to do this is to look at the whole board and come up with the representations for one 8, and for two 8s. These models are abcd8 (for the set **and** full house and bigger above 8s hands), and abc88. With 50 cards, the total number of five card combinations is 50*49*48*47*46/5*4*3*2*1= 2,118,760. Disregarding the two remaining 8s, we have 48 cards which can be combined into four card combinations (abcd). The total number of four card combinations is 48*47*46*45/4*3*2*1= 194,580. Each of those four card combinations may combine with either of the remaining 8s, giving 2*194,580= 389,160 combinations containing an 8. For 88, the number of three card combinations which can be made from 48 cards is 48*47*46/3*2*1= 17296, giving us 17296 quad 8s combinations. The total number of combinations containing either an 8 or two 8s is 194,580+17296= 406,456. The probability of seeing one of those combinations on the boards is 406456/2,118,760= .1918= **19.2%**.

Again, this **overall** figure can be arrived at by combining probabilities. For the flop, the probability of not hitting an 8 was .882. For the remaining 47 cards, the probability of not hitting any of the two 8s is 45/47*44/46= 1980/2162= .916. The combined probability of not hitting an 8 is .882*.916= .808= 80.8%. The probability of making at least a set, if you go to the river, is 100-80.8= **19.2%**.

Now, if you're the shotgun type, this would've have been a lot less work. You've got two outs with five cards to come. That gives you 10 shots out of 50 to improve your hand, or 10/50= 20%.

That is a fairly complete picture of the pocket pair.

TABLE FOR A POCKET PAIR

	# combos	%	Odds
The probability of being dealt:			
a pocket pair	78/1326	5.9	16:1
a specific pair (e.g., KK)	6/ @	.5	220:1
Holding a pocket pair, the			
probability of flopping:			
a set (one on flop)	2112/19600	10.8	8.3:1
a full house	144/ @	.74	136:1
quads	48/ @	.25	407:1
at least a set (2112+144+48)	2304/ @	11.8	7.5:1

Beyond the flop:

	# combos	%	Odds
With a set on the flop, the hand will improve to at least a full house	361/1081	33	2:1
Probability of set improving to a full house on the turn	7/47*	15	5.7:1
Probability of set improving to a full house on the river	10/46*	22	3.6:1
Probability of pocket pair improving to a set with one card to come	2/46*	4.4	22:1

No fold'em Hold'em:

	# combos	%	Odds
At least a set will be made if your pocket pair is taken to the river	406,456/**	19	4.2:1

* number of outs
** of a total 2,118,760 combinations

SUITED CARDS

Looking down and seeing AK suited quickens the pulse. Seeing two more of the same suit on the flop with heavy multi-way action makes you a major contender for the pot and cranks up the strategist in you. The flush draw will be completed **35%** of the time with two cards to come. Often, when the flush is missed, you end up with a weak or nothing hand, costing you a small fortune in the process. Other days, made flushes and big wins often go together.

FLUSHES
All the following work is done by combinations in complete detail-it is a complete course on the anatomy of a flush. For the beginners, it will always be here for your reference; for others, use it as you will.

There are 13 cards available from which to make a flush. The total possible number of flushes for any suit is 13*12*11*10*9/5*4*3*2*1= 15440/120= **1287**. Of that number, **10** are straight flushes, leaving **1277** flushes in each suit which are beaten by any full house. The total number of flushes for all suits is 1287*4= 5148. Since the total possible number of five card poker hands is 52*51*50*49*48/5*4*3*2*1= 2,598,960, the odds against being dealt a flush in the first five cards are (2,598,960-5148):5148= **504:1**. Of course, your chances of making a flush in seven cards are improved and are covered for every stage of the hand, and for every situation, in the following paragraphs and are summarized in the accompanying table.

HOLE CARDS
Getting two suited cards as your starting hand is a fairly common occurrence. The total possible number of two card starting hands is 52*51/2*1= 1326. The number of combinations which are suited, for the 13 cards of any suit, is 13*12/2*1= 78. The number of suited combinations for four suits is 4*78= 312. The odds of getting suited cards are (1326-312):312= **3.25:1**. The probability of getting suited cards is 312/1326= 23.53%= **24%**. For those who play **any** two suited cards, there is plenty of opportunity to play. **Making** a flush is a lot more difficult as we'll see. With suited cards, the flop can go either of four ways with respect to the flush.

FLOP
Flopping a flush. Since there are 11 flush cards remaining, the number of three card suited combinations which will flop a flush is 11*10*9/3*2*1= 990/6= 165. The total possible number of flops with the remaining 50 cards (you hold two in your hand) is 50*49*48/3*2*1= 19600. The odds of

flopping a flush are (19600-165):165= **118:1**, or a probability of 165/19600= **.842%**.

Flopping a four flush. With 11 cards remaining, the number of two card flush combinations is represented by the model ffx, where ff represent flush cards, and x is any of the other 39 remaining cards not of your suit. The number of ff combinations with 11 cards remaining is 11*10/2*1= 55. Any of those 55 combinations may combine with any of the 39 other cards, giving 55*39= 2145 ffx combinations. Note that a number of those combinations will be pairs. The odds of hitting a four flush are (19600-2145):2145= **8.14:1**. The probability of hitting a four flush is 2145/19600= 10.944%= approximately **11%**.

Flopping one of your suit. With 11 cards remaining, the number of single flush card combinations is represented by the model fxy, where f is any of the 11 flush cards and xy is any two card combination from the other 39 cards, including a pair. The number of xy combinations for 39 cards is 39*38/2*1= 741. The number of fxy combinations is 11*741= 8151. At this point, be aware that a number of those fxy combinations are of the type f77, others are three of a kind, and a number of the combinations pairs the flush card as well. You could strip out those combinations to arrive at the number of fxy combinations, where fxy are of different ranks. In the interests of sanity, I will not do it here, but you now have the tools and thinking that are required to do it. Back to the work. The odds of flopping only one of your suit are (19600-8151):8151= **1.4:1**. The probability of doing so is 8151/19600= **41.6%**.

Flopping none of your suit. To determine the chances of missing your suit completely, calculate the number of three card combinations possible with the other 39 'offsuit' cards. The number of three card combinations for 39 cards is 39*38*37/3*2*1= 9139. All the rest of the combinations contain one, two, or three of your suit. The odds of hitting none of your suit are (19600-9139):9139= **1.145:1**, or a probability of **46.6%**. In other words, just under **half the time**, you will not flop any part of your flush draw. If 9139 three card combinations contain no flush cards, then the number of combinations which contain one, two, or three flush cards must be 19600-9139= 10,461. To verify the numbers, add the one, two, and three suit combinations from above: 165+2145+8151= 10,461. Voila. The latter example of missing a flush card completely can be done by combining probabilities and serves as a check on our work with combinations. Quickly, the probability of hitting none of your suit is 39/50*38/49*37/48= 54834/117600= **46.6%**.

OFFSUIT CARDS

In the examples above, we started with two suited cards. Sometimes, we have only one high suited card, and the flop comes in such a way as to keep us in: three suited cards on the flop, or, we make a pair and two of our suits are on the flop, and we have a back door flush possibility. In those cases where we hold only one card of the suit of interest, the number of remaining flush cards is 12.

The number of three card combinations which the remaining 12 flush cards can make is 12*11*10/3*2*1= 220. The odds against flopping three of our suit are (19600-220):220= **88:1** or a probability of 220/19600= **1.12%**.

The number of two card combinations which can be made from the remaining 12 flush cards is 12*11/2*1= 66. Since any one of those combinations may combine with any of the remaining 48-10= 38 cards, we have 38*66= 2508 three card combinations containing two of our flush cards. The odds against flopping two of our suit are (19600-2508):2508= **6.8:1**, or a probability of 2508/19600= **12.8%**.

TWO TO COME

There are a number of ways to proceed and make a flush, or keep on making a flush. If you are holding two suited cards in your hand, you may flop a flush and want no more to come, a **dout** situation, (see, **TABLE OF TWO TO COME**, 8 outs, for the odds of having your flush destroyed), or you may want another flush card so that someone else can make a weaker flush (see same table, 7 outs, or 6 outs if there are two other players).

If you've flopped a four flush, one or two outs may come, (see same table, 9 outs) and in this case you may want one, but not two, or you may want two, so someone else can make a second best flush (8 outs).

You also have nine outs if you have one high suit in your hand and three on the flop. In this case, either one or two flush cards may come (see same table, 9 outs).

If you have one in your hand and two on the flop, or two in your hand and one on the flop, you may get two of your suits running, as depicted on the next page.

This one we will calculate. After the flop, there are 47 cards remaining and 47*46/2*1= 1081 possible two card combinations. Of those 47 cards, 10 are the flush cards which we desire. The number of two flush card combinations is 10*9/2*1= 45. The odds of getting two running, suited cards are (1081-45):45= **23:1**. The probability of doing so is 45/1081= **4.2%**. We could have also used, **THE TABLE OF TWO TO COME**, and looked at 10 outs and the probability of hitting two outs.

For completeness, you have two suited cards and a different suit flush is on board. With 50 cards, the number of five card combinations is 50*49*48*47*46/5*4*3*2*1= 2,118,760. The number of five card flushes for any suit is 1287. The number of flushes for the other three suits is 1287*3= 3861. The probability that this will happen is 3861/2,118,760= **.18%**, or odds of against of (2,118,760-3861):3861= **548:1**.

After all that work, let's tabulate the above into some reasonable situations.

TABLE OF FLUSHES

SITUATION 1	# combos	%	ODDS
You have two suited cards:			
chance of flopping a four flush	2145/19600	11	8.1:1
then, chance of hitting one or two suits	378/1081	35	1.9:1
or, chance of hitting only one suit	342/ @	32	
HITTING FLOP and RIVER**		3.8	25:1
OR			
chance of flopping a flush	165/19600	.84	118:1
then, chance of one or two more suits	340/ @	31.5	2.2:1
OR			
chance of flopping one suit	8151/19600	41.6	1.4:1
then, chance of two running suits	45/1081	4.2	23:1
HITTING FLOP and RIVER***		1.7	55:1
OR			
chance of flopping none of your suit	9139/19600	46.6	1.1:1
OR			
chance of a different suit flush on board	3861/****	.2	548:1

** it is 2145/19600*378/1081= 810810/21,187,600= 3.8%- an example of combining probabilities by combinations, or if slight error is permissible, then quick approximation of .11*.35= 3.85% by combining probabilities of probabilities

*** it is 8151/19600*45/1081= 366795/21,187,600= 1.7%- another example of combining probabilities by combinations, or if slight error is permissible, then quick approximation of .416*.042=1.75% by combining probabilities of probabilities.

****2,118,760

continued on next page

SITUATION 2	# combos	%	ODDS
You have offsuit cards*:			
chance of flopping three same suits**	220/19600	1.1	88:1
then, chance of hitting one or two suits	378/1081	35	1.9:1
HITTING FLOP and RIVER*		.39	249:1

OR

chance of flopping two same suits**	2508/19600	12.8	6.8:1
then, chance of hitting two running suits	45/1081	4.2	23:1
HITTING FLOP and RIVER**		.53	184:1

* and therefore, only one of the cards will be involved in making a flush in the situations described. If you have two high offsuit cards, e.g., AK, also see discussion next page.

** that match one of your cards

*** it is 220/19600*378/1081= 83,160/21,187,600= .39%, or if slight error is permissible, then quick approximation of .011*.35= .385%

**** it is 2508/19600*45/1081= 112,860/21,187,600= .53%, or if slight error is permissible, then quick approximation of .128*.042= .538%

Also see DISCUSSION on following pages for adavantage of suited cards over offsuit cards.

DISCUSSION

In poker literature, one often comes across advice such as reraise a raiser if you hold AK suited. The presumption seems to be, that these cards suited are much more powerful than if they were offsuit. Again, when dealing with suited cards, it is stated by various authors that suited cards give an advantage of four or five per cent. Of course, this extra advantage comes from the greater flush making possibility when starting with suited cards. Let us examine in more detail the advantage of starting with suited cards and try to quantify that advantage. To do so, we will look at two situations: first, we will deal with AK suited versus AK offsuit, and then look at 78 suited versus 78 offsuit. The numbers in, **TABLE OF FLUSHES** will be used.

AK SUITED vs AK OFFSUIT

When starting with suited cards, you only need three of the five board cards to be in your suit; with two offsuit cards you need four of the five board cards to be of your suit. However, note that for two offsuit cards, you can make two different flushes: one will give you the nut flush and the other will give you a second nut (King high) flush, barring any straight flushes.

With AK suited, you can make a flush three different ways if carried through to the river: by flopping it; by flopping a four flush and hitting one or two of your suit on the turn and/or river; by flopping one of your suit and hitting two running suits. With AK offsuit, you can make a flush two different ways if carried through to the river: by flopping three of your suit and hitting another of your suit on the turn or river; by flopping two of your suit and hitting two running suits. Note that with AK offsuit, these scenarios could happen for either of your two starting cards. At this point, some readers will object that they rarely try to backdoor a flush (catch two running suits on the turn and river). That is probably true if you have missed the flop completely and going further is hopeless. However, if you do have a piece of the flop and now catch another of your suit on the turn, you have increased your chances of winning. In loose games such as those found in Toronto, many players pay to take another card off after the flop on the backdoor possibility alone. Having said all of the above, we now have the basis on which to quantify the maximum advantage of AK suited over AK offsuit. This will be done by adding up all the chances by which a flush can be made for AK suited and AK offsuit and subtracting the latter from the former.

For AK suited, the probability of flopping a flush is .84%. Done. The probability of flopping a four flush is 11% and the chance of completing it by the river is 35%, for a combined probability of 3.8%. The probability of flopping one suit is 41.6% and the probability of getting two running suits is 4.2%, for a combined probability of 1.7%. The total probability of making a flush taking AK suited to the river is .84+3.8+1.7= **6.34%**. This figure must now be compared to the flush possibilities for AK offsuit.

For AK offsuit, the probability of flopping three of your suit is 1.1%, and the chance of getting one or two of your suits is 35%, for a combined probability of .39%. The probability of flopping two of your suit is 12.8% and the probability of hitting two running suits is 4.2%, for a combined probability of .53%. The total probability of making a flush taking AK offsuit to the river is .39+.53= **.92%**. If you choose to discount the King high flush possibility calculate no further. However, if you consider a King high flush made with four of the suit on board as a reasonable hand and most of us would, then multiply by two (either the A or the K can make a flush) to give **2*.92= 1.84%**. Most players will appreciate that the King high flush is beaten by an Ace high flush.

Summarizing, the advantage of AK suited over AK offsuit is **6.34-1.84= 4.5%** for the **two flushes** possibility of AK offsuit. When considering only the single flush possibility for AK offsuit, the advantage increases to **6.34-.92= 5.42%**. Whether these advantages of AK suited over AK offsuit warrants reraising a raiser is, alas, beyond the scope of this book and better left to strategists and tacticians more skilled than myself. However, if you are reraising to get free cards, then you would presumably do the same for AK offsuit. When we compare Ax suited to Ax offsuit, where x is a Queen or lower, the second flush possibility will progressively be discounted. The advantage of these suited cards over the same cards offsuit is **6.34-.92= 5.42%**.

78 SUITED vs 78 OFFSUIT

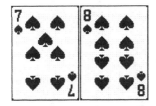 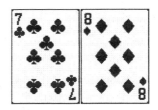

In considering 78 suited over 78 offsuit, the situation is easier to deal with, since you almost would certainly not want to make a flush in **both** cases if there were four of the same suit on the board. Therefore, for purposes of comparison, I will disregard all situations where there are four of the same suit on the board.

For 78 suited, the probability of flopping a flush is **.84%**. Done. The probability of flopping a four flush is 11% and the probability of hitting **only one** of your suit with two cards to come is 32% (see **TABLE OF TWO TO COME**, 9 outs, hitting one out only) for a combined probability of 2145*342/21,187,600= **3.46%**. The probability of flopping one of your suit is 41.6% and the probability of two running suits is 4.2%, for a combined probability of **1.7%**. The total probability of making a five card flush if the situation warrants taking 78 suited to the river is .84+3.46+1.7= **6%**.

Since we have assumed that we do not want to make a flush when holding 78 offsuit, the advantage of 78 suited over 78 offsuit is **6%**. As to interpretation of that figure, most authors will say that 78 is a weak holding that should only be played multiway, and only with that **6%** advantage, i.e., suited. I agree.

OFFSUIT CARDS

In this annex, the area of primary concern is with making a pair, two pairs, trips, and full houses. As discussed in the annex, **HOLE CARDS**, 71%, or 936 of the total possible number of 1326 starting hands will be offsuit cards. That means, that most often we will be hoping to catch a pair or two pair by the end of the hand. Of course, the same two ranks, whether offsuit or suited, both have the same potential for pairing. For flush and straight probabilities, see the applicable annexes, **SUITED CARDS**, and, **CONNECTORS**.

THE FLOP

Flopping one Pair. Assume you're holding KJ offsuit. What are the chances of hitting a pair on the flop? First, determine the total possible number of flops with the 50 remaining cards. The total possible number of three card combinations with 50 cards is 50*49*48/3*2*1= 19600. A certain number of those combinations will contain one or more Jacks, one or more Kings, some combination of Ks and Js, all Js or all Ks, and a large number of combinations will contain neither. The model for a pair is Kxy or Jxy, where xy is any two card combination drawn from the remaining 44 cards (no Ks or Js). The number of two card combinations is 44*43/2*1=

1892/2= 946. Each of those 946 two card combinations can have as its third card any of the remaining three Js or three Ks. The total possible number of **one pair** combinations is 6*946= 5676. The probability of making one pair on the flop is 5676/19600= 28.96= 29%, and the odds against it are (19600-5676):5676= 2.45:1= 2.5:1. That's the **AK** hope. The above number cannot be verified by combining probabilities; that method can only tell you the probability of making **at least** a pair on the flop. We **will** verify our aggregate number later on.

Flopping Two Pair. To determine the probability of flopping two pair, i.e., a K and J on the flop, we first need to determine the total possible number of two card combinations with the three Js and three Ks. That number is 6*5/2*1= 30/2= 15. From that number, we must strip out the JJ and KK combinations for now. The number of JJ pairs which can be made from three Js is 3*2/2*1= 3. The same is true for the Ks. Therefore, the number of KJ combinations is 15-3-3= 9. Since any of the nine KJ combinations can have any of the remaining 44 cards as the third part of the flop, the number of flops containing KJ is 9*44= 396. The probability of making Ks and Js on the flop is 396/19600= 2.02%. The odds against making those two pairs on the flop are (19600-396):396= 48.5:1= 49:1.

Flopping Trips.

The probability of making trip Js (model is JJx, where x is any of the remaining 44 cards) is the three JJ combinations multiplied by the 44 remaining cards, i.e., 3*44= 132. The probability of doing so is 132/19600= .67%= .7%, or odds against of (19600-132):132= 147.5:1= **148:1**. The probability of making either trip Js or trip Ks is (132+132)/19600= 264/19600= 1.35%, or odds against of **73:1**.

Flopping a Full House. The probability of making Js full, i.e., JJK, is the three JJ combinations (3*2/2*1= 3) combined with any of the three Ks, or 3*3=9, over 19600. Solving, the probability is 9/19600= .046%, or odds against of (19600-9):9= 19591:9= 2177:1. The probability of making either Js full of Ks, or Ks full of Js, is 18/19600= .092%, or odds against of (19600-18):18= 19582:18= **1087:1**.

Flopping Quads. The probability of flopping either quad Js or quad Ks, i.e., JJJ or KKK, is 2/19600= .01%, or odds against of 19598:2= **9799:1**.

All the flop possibilities for K and J with respect to pairing and stronger have been taken care of. If we total all the above possibilities, we can verify the total number of possible combinations by combining probabilities. All the combinations from above are 5676 (one pair), 396 (two pair), 264 (trips), 18 (full houses), and 2 (quads), which gives us a total of 6356. The probability of making at least a pair on the flop is 6356/19600= 32.43%. To verify, we will combine the probabilities of not hitting a J or a K (six cards) on the flop. For the first card, the probability of not hitting a K or J is (50-6)/50= 44/50. If we

do not hit a K or J, then for the second card, the probability is 43/49, and for the third card it is 42/48. The probability of not hitting a K or J on the flop is the combined probabilities, or
44/50*43/49*42/48= 79464/117600= 67.57%. The probability of making at least a pair is 100-67.57= 32.43%. Voila. **The probability of not making anything pair related on the flop is 100-32.43= 67.57= 67.6= 68%.**

BEYOND THE FLOP
   With the flop done, we can turn our attention to the situations for the turn and river. The, **TABLE OF TWO TO COME**, will be useful for this work. The situations we will look at: missing the flop completely and continuing on; you have a pair on the flop and believe either two pair or trips will win; you have two pair on the flop and need to make a full house to win; or you have trips on the flop and need a full house or better to win.
   If you hold K and J offsuit, and the flop is low and ragged, i.e., you missed the flop, what is the probability of making a pair with your two overcards and two cards to come? Consulting the, **TABLE OF TWO TO COME**, for six outs, you have a **24.1%** probability of hitting one or two of your outs, or odds against of **3.2:1**.
   If you missed the flop, the probability of making **two pairs or trips**, means that you **must hit two** of your **six** outs. From the, **TABLE OF TWO TO COME**, that probability is 15/1081= **1.4%**, or odds against of (1081-15):15= **71:1**.
   If you make one pair on the flop, say Js,

and either two pair or trips will win, then you have three Ks and two Js to make your hand, or five outs. The probability of hitting one or two of your outs is **20.3%**.

If you make two pair on the flop and need a full house to win, you must hit either of the two remaining Js or Ks. With four outs, the probability of hitting either one or two of your outs is **16.5%**.

If you make trips on the flop, say KK4, and need a full house or better to win, the situation is the same as for having made a set on the flop (i.e., a pocket pair with one of the same kind on the flop) with respect to the number of outs. You can make a totally different running pair, hit a K for quads, hit one of the three remaining Js or one of the three remaining 4s, or hit a J and a 4. See the annex, **THE POCKET PAIR**, to find out how we arrive at a **33.4%** probability of making a full house. You can also use the, **TABLE OF TWO TO COME**, and use the number for seven outs. That gives a probability of 27.8%. BUT, that does not account for the possibility of making an unrelated running pair. Stripping out the Ks, Js, and 4s, there are 10 other ranks from which to make pairs. The number of different pairs which 10 ranks can make is 10*6= 60. The total number of two card combinations from the remaining 47 cards is 47*46/2*1= 1081. The probability of hitting an unrelated running pair is 60/1081= 5.6%. The probability of making a full house with two cards to come is 27.8+5.6= **33.4%**.

The above material is tabulated in the following appendix.

PAIRS, TRIPS, AND FULL HOUSES

WHEN HOLDING TWO DIFFERENT RANKS,	# combos	%	Odds
chances of flopping*:			
one pair	5676/19600	29	2.5:1
two pairs	396/ @	2	49:1
trips	264/ @	1.4	73:1
a full house	18/ @	.1	1087:1
quads	2/ @	.01	9799:1
at least a pair	6356/ @	32	2.1:1
no pair	13244/ @	68	.5:1
BEYOND THE FLOP			
two to come, missed flop:			
to make at least one pair	261/1081	24	3.2:1
to make two pairs or trips	15/ @	1.4	71:1
two to come, one pair on flop:			
to make just two pairs (3 outs)**	132/1081	12	7.2:1
to make two pair or better(5 outs)*	220/ @	20	3.9:1
two to come, two pairs on flop:			
to make at least a full house	178/1081	17	5:1
two to come, trips on flop:			
to make a full house	361/1081	33	2:1
AFTER THE TURN			
One to come, two pairs at turn:			
to make a full house	4/46***	8.7	10.5:1
One to come, set (trips) at turn:			
to make a full house, quads	10/46***	22	3.6:1

*hands related to your hole cards
**two pair made by pairing your hole cards
***number of outs

137

CONNECTORS

STRAIGHTS

When looking down and seeing JT offsuit with five callers, the thought of making a straight comes to mind. The straight is the bastard cousin to the straight flush. Lay out the cards as follows: A23456789TJQKA.

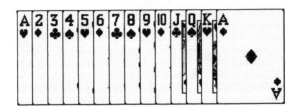

From left to right, taken five at a time, there are 10 different straights which can be made: A to 5, 2 to 6, 3 to 7,...,T to A. For each kind of straight, there are 1024 variations. Of that number, four are straight flushes. The total possible number of straights which are beaten by any flush is 10(1024-4)= 10200.

The straight is street smart and can come at you in a few different ways: it can be completed by starting open-ended, incredibly well-disguised as a double-belly buster, or, right in the gut as an inside straight. Often, your bet on the end with top pair and good kicker gets raised and a straight is shown down. But, how likely is it that we will end up with a straight? Let's look at the anatomy of a straight from start to finish by taking a look at offsuit connectors. For the case of starting with suited connectors, including one-gaps, where you can flop flushes and/or straights, flushes and/or straight draws, see the annex, **SUITED CONNECTORS**. In the material to follow, I will be emphasizing offsuit connectors. This is not because there is something wrong with suited connectors, they can make straights just as easily as offsuit connectors, but, because I do not want to deal with subtracting combinations that would flop flushes and four flushes in **this** annex. The focus here is with straights.

CONNECTORS AND STRETCH

If we look at the cards laid out on the previous page, and consider them two at a time as our hole cards, we will see that some offer greater straight making potential, or greater "**stretch**" than others. First, the number of two card connectors is 13: A2, 23, ...QK, and KA. If you hold 23, the straights which you can make using both your hole cards are A2345, and 23456, i.e., two straights. If you hold TJ, the straights which you can make using both your hole cards are 789TJ, 89TJQ, 9TJQK, and TJQKA, i.e., four straights. The connectors which are capable of making four straights have **maximum** stretch; there are at least three ranks below and three ranks above the connector. The connectors meeting this criteria are **45, 56, 67, 78, 89, 9T**, and **TJ**-seven in all. The connectors A2 and AK have **minimum** stretch and can make only one straight each, using both cards. QK and 23 can make two straights, while 34 and JQ can make three straights, again, using both cards. Note that if you hold JT as your hole cards and a straight is made, and there is neither a Jack nor a Ten on the board, you have the **nut** straight. The formula for the number of straights which can be made using your two connectors is to count the number of ranks above to a maximum of three, and the number of ranks below to a maximum of three, add the two numbers together, and subtract two. Using JQ as an example, there are two ranks above (K and A) and three ranks below (89T), giving five ranks. Therefore, 5-2= 3 straights can be made. For 23, there are three ranks above and one rank below totalling four ranks. Therefore, 4-2= 2 straights can be made.

CONNECTORS AS STARTING HANDS

How probable is it that you will get connectors as a starting hand? Take AK as an example. From our previous work, we know that the four Ks and four As can make 16 AK combinations, of which four are suited. The same will be true for any other connectors. Since there are 13 two card connectors, the total number of connectors is 13*16= **208**. The probability of being dealt connectors is 208/1326= .157= **15.7%**. The number of suited connectors is 13*4= 72. The number of connectors with **maximum stretch** is 7*16= **112**. The probability of being dealt connectors with maximum stretch is 112/1326 = **8.5%**. The number of suited connectors with maximum stretch is 7*4= 28, and the probability of being dealt one is 28/1326= **2.1%**. For the probabilities of making one pair, two pairs, trips, etc., see the annex, **OFFSUIT CARDS**.

CONNECTORS WITH MAX STRETCH

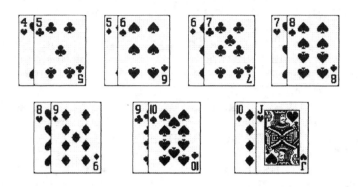

If we look again at the max stretch connectors, say TJ offsuit for example, and consider only the flop for the moment, we see that a number of straights and straight draws can be flopped: four straights- 789TJ, 89TJQ, 9TJQK, and TJQKA; three open-ended straight draws (8 outs)- x89TJ, x9TJQ, and xTJQK; two double belly buster (DBB) straight draws of 8 outs- 79TJK, and 8TJQA; and six inside straight draws of 4 outs- 7x9TJ, 78xTJ, 8xTJQ, 9TJxK, TJxKA and TJQxA. That adds up to a mountain of possibilities.

FLOPPING A STRAIGHT

If you are holding JcTs, what is the probability of flopping a 789TJ straight? To calculate this probability we need to determine the total possible number of flops with the 50 remaining cards, and then determine the number of 789 sequences, any order, which can be made from all the 7s, 8s, and 9s.

The total possible number of flops with 50 cards is 50*49*48/3*2*1= 19600. From the chapter, **REFERENCE COMBINATIONS**, the number of 789 sequences for the 7s, 8s, and 9s is 64. The probability of flopping this straight is 64/19600= .003= .3%. Since the same will be true for 89Q, 9QK, and QKA, the probability of flopping one of the four straights possible when holding JT is 4*64/19600= 256/19600= **1.3%**. The same methodology and figures will be true for any connectors with max stretch.

It might be tempting to try and solve this problem by the big picture approach, and say that there are 1024 straights of this type, out of a possible 2,598,960 five card hands. Then, the probability of being dealt this straight in the first five cards is 1024/19600= .000394%. Using this logic, the same would be true of the other three straights. The probability of being dealt a straight with JT would then be 4*.000394= .0016%. This answer is **incorrect**, because the situations are different. In the first example, it is a given that we already hold JT, two fifths of our straight, and we only need three cards in sequence to complete the straight. In the big picture, we start with nothing, and need to get all five straight cards.

FLOPPING AN OPEN-ENDED STRAIGHT DRAW

If you are holding JcTs, determine the probability of flopping x89TJ, i.e., an open-ended straight draw, where x is any card except a 7 or a Q (the 7 or Q would make a straight on the flop). Note, that by definition, we include the possibility that our open-ended straight draw may have x as an 8,9, i.e., a pair on board. Also note that this includes the possibility of making a four flush when x89 is all clubs or all spades. We will quantify those combinations later. To calculate this probability, we need to determine the number of 89 combinations and multiply that number by x, which is reduced by 8 cards (the four 7s and four Qs).

The total possible number of flops with the 50 remaining cards is 19600. From our work with AK, we know that the number of 89 combinations is 16 (8*7/2*1-6-6= 16). Any of those 16 combinations may combine with any card which is x. With 48 cards available (you hold TcJs and an 89 will be on the board), and where x cannot be a 7 or a Q, x= 48-8= 40. The number of x89 combinations is 16*40= 640. The probability of the flop coming x89TJ is 640/19600= 3.3%.

As promised, the number of three club flops containing 89 of clubs which do not flop a straight is eight (89 combining with 23456TK and A of clubs). The same is true for 89 of spades (23456JK and A). These 8+8= 16 combinations produce both an open-ended straight **and** flush draw.

The probability of flopping x9TJQ and xTJQK is exactly the same as for x89TJ. Therefore, the probability of flopping an open-ended straight draw when holding JT offsuit is 3*640/19600= 1920/19600= .098= **9.8%**

If we want to know the probability of flopping a non-pairing open-ended straight draw of the type x89TJ, we would have to further reduce x by six (three each of 8s and 9s). The probability of flopping an open-ended, non-pairing straight draw of the type x89TJ is x*16/19600, where x= 40-6= 34, giving 34*16/19600= 544/19600= .028= **2.8%**. The same would be true for x9TJQ and xTJQK. The probability of flopping an open-ended straight draw without a pair on board is 3*544/19600= 1632/19600= .083= **8.3%**.

If we want to know the probability of flopping a non-pairing, open-ended straight draw, and where we also do not pair the board with our starting hand of JcTs, we would have to further reduce x by six (three each of Js and Ts). The probability of flopping this open-ended straight draw is x*16/19600, where x= 34-6= 28, giving 28*16/19600= 448/19600= .023= **2.3%**. The same would be true for x9TJQ and xTJQK. The probability of flopping this very clean, drawing to the nuts, type of straight draw for JT is 3*448/19600= 1344/19600= .069= **6.9%**. Note that for the other max stretch connectors, not all these clean, open-ended straight draws will be to the nuts.

FLOPPING A DBB STRAIGHT DRAW

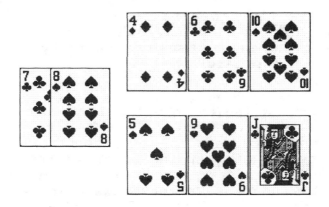

If you are holding 7c8s, determine the probability of flopping a DBB straight draw. To get this draw of eight outs, the flop must come 46T, (with a 5 or 9 on the turn or river to make the straight), or 59J (a 6 or T on the turn or river to make the straight). To solve for the case of 46T, determine the number of 46T combinations which can be made from all the 4s, 6s, and Ts and put that number over 19600.

From our previous work with the four 7s, 8s, and 9s in the chapter, **REFERENCE COMBINATIONS**, the number of non-pairing, non-tripping combinations which can be made is 64. The same holds true for the 4s, 6s, and Ts. The probability of flopping this DBB straight draw is 64/19600= .003= .3%. Note that one of those 46T combinations will be all clubs and one will be all spades. Those two combinations result in a DBB straight draw **and** a four flush.

The probability of flopping either of the two DBB straight draws while holding 7c8s is 2*64/19600= 128/19600= .0065= .65%. Note that in order to flop a DBB straight draw, you must hit three cards, **exactly** the same situation, and same probability, as for flopping a straight.

FLOPPING AN INSIDE STRAIGHT DRAW

If you are holding 56 offsuit (a max stretch connector), determine the probability of flopping an inside straight draw. For this max stretch connector, there are six inside straight draws which can be flopped: 2x456, 23x56, 3x567, 456x8, 56x89, and 567x9. Looking only at the case of 2x456, we need to determine the number of 2 and 4 combinations, and multiply that by x, where x can be any of the remaining cards, but cannot be a 3.

The total possible number of flops with 50 cards is 50*49*48/3*2*1= 19600. The total number of 2 and 4 combinations is 16 (see work on AK). Any of those combinations can combine with x, where x= 48-4= 44. The number of 2x456 inside straight draws is 16*44= 704. The probability of getting this inside straight draw is 704/19600= .036= 3.6%. The probability of getting any of the six possible inside straight draws while holding 56 offsuit is 6*704/19600= 4224/19600= **21.6%**. Note that it is easier to flop an inside straight draw than an open-ended straight draw, **but,** more difficult to complete the inside straight draw (four outs vs eight outs).

FLOPPING A STRAIGHT OR A STRAIGHT DRAW

The probability of flopping a straight, or an eight outs straight draw (open-ended and DBB), for a max stretch connector, is the sum of their combinations, i.e, the sum of their probabilities. That probability is (256+ 1920+ 128)/19600= 2304/19600= .118= 11.8%.

If you're the type of player who goes after any straight draw including inside straight draws, then add 4224 more combinations for a probability of (2304+ 4224)/19600= 6528/19600= .33= 33%. The odds against making a straight, or an eight outs straight draw, or a four outs straight draw are only 19600-6528:6528= 2:1

COMPLETING THE DRAWS

With two cards to come, the probability of completing an eight outs straight draw by hitting one or two of your outs is 31.5%, or odds against of 2.2:1. The probability of completing an inside straight draw by hitting one or two of your outs is 16.5%, or odds against of 5:1, with two cards to come. Numbers from the, TABLE OF TWO TO COME.

MIDDLE STRETCH CONNECTORS

FLOPPING A STRAIGHT

For the middle stretch connectors of 34 JQ offsuit, the maximum number of straights which can be flopped is three. Using the basic methodology and numbers from above of 64 three card sequences for every possible straight, we have the probability of either flopping a straight as 3*64/19600= 192/19600= .0098= .98%= **1%**.

FLOPPING AN OPEN-ENDED STRAIGHT DRAW

The number of open-ended straight draws which 34 or JQ offsuit can flop is two. Using the numbers and methodology from above, we have the probability of either flopping an open-ended straight draw as 2*640/19600= 1280/19600= **6.5%**.

FLOPPING A DBB STRAIGHT DRAW

The number of DBB straight draws which 34 or JQ offsuit can flop is one: for 34, it is A57, and for JQ it is 8TA. The probability of either flopping the DBB straight draw is 64/19600= **.33%**.

FLOPPING AN INSIDE STRAIGHT DRAW

The number of inside straight draws which either 34 or JQ offsuit can flop is four. For 34 we have Ax345, 234x6, **34**x67 and 345x7. For JQ we have 8xTJQ, 89x**JQ**, 9xJQK, and TJQxA. Using the numbers and methodology from above, we have the probability of either flopping an inside straight draw as 4*704/19600= 2816/19600= **14.4%**.

COMPLETING THE DRAW

With two cards to come, the probability of making the draws is given in, **TABLE OF TWO TO COME**.

LOW AND MIN STRETCH CONNECTORS

For 23 and QK offsuit, the number of straights which can be made is two. Using the basic methodology and numbers from above of 64 three card sequences for every possible straight, we have the probability of flopping a straight with either of these connectors as 2*64/19600= 128/19600= .0065= .65%

These connectors can flop only one open-ended straight draw. The probability of flopping an open-ended straight draw for either 23 or QK is 640/19600= .033= **3.3%**.

There is no DBB straight draw for these connectors.

The number of four-out straight draws is four: for 23 we have A234x, A23x5, 23x56, and 234x6; for QK we have 9xJQK, 9TxQK, TxQKA, and TJQKx. The probability of flopping a four-out straight draw for either case is 4*704/19600= 2816/19600= **14.4%**.

Finally, for A2 and KA, only one straight can be flopped. The probability of flopping a straight is 64/19600= .33%. Neither an open-ended nor a DBB straight draw is possible. A2 and KA can flop three four-out straight draws: for A2 we have **A2x45**, **A23x5** and **A234x**; for KA we have **TxQKA**, **TJxKA**, and **xJQKA**. The probability of either connector flopping these straight draws is 3*704/19600= 2112/19600= .108= **10.8%**.

COMPLETING THE DRAW
    With two cards to come, the probability of making the draws is given in, **TABLE OF TWO TO COME.**

CONCLUSIONS
    Max stretch connectors have relatively high probabilities of flopping a hand and/or a draw. All the preceding material is summarized in the following table.

MAX STRETCH CONNECTORS*
(the group of seven)

	# combos	%	Odds
Probability of receiving max connector as starting hand (suited and offsuit)	112/1326	8.5	11:1

For any of the seven, the probability of flopping:

	# combos	%	Odds
a straight	256/19600	1.3	76:1
AN open-ended straight draw	1920/ @	9.8	9:1
A DBB straight draw**	128/ @	.65	152:1
AN eight outs straight draw, (open-ended or DBB str draw)	2048/ @	10.5	8.6:1
A straight or eight outs straight draw (256+2048)	2304/ @	11.8	7.5:1
AN inside straight draw	4224/ @	21.6	3.6:1
A straight or eight outs str draw or inside str draw	6528/ @	33	2:1
A clean, open-ended straight draw (for JT, a nut draw)	1344/ @	6.9	14:1

Probability to complete with two cards to come:

	# combos	%	Odds
EIGHT outs straight draw	340/1081	31.5	2.2:1
FOUR outs straight draw	178/ @	16.5	5:1

@ is the number directly above
* 45, 56, 67, 78, 89, 9T, and TJ can all flop four straights, and three open-ended, two DBB, and six inside, straight draws.
** The DBB straight draw flops are:
for 45-A37 and 268// for 56-248 and 379// for 67-359 and 48T//
for 78-46T and 59J// for 89-57J and 6TQ// for 9T-68Q and 7JK//
for TJ-79K and 8QA

SUITED CONNECTORS

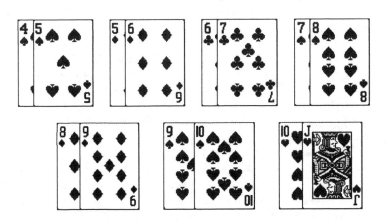

In Toronto, where the action is loose (see the annex, **TORONTO HOLD'EM**), these cards are typically played by weak players from any position, and even heads-up against an early position raiser. For those players, suited connectors possess magical power and are played **religiously**. For stronger players, suited connectors possess potential which can profitably be played from certain positions under certain conditions (typically, if in late position, if there is a sufficient number of players in the pot, if the pot has not been raised, etc.,). Let's analyze this holding of suited connectors, sequenced and one-gap, having **maximum** stretch, and quantify the probabilities for flopping a big hand, i.e., the flush or the straight; or, for flopping a draw- the four flush **or** eight outs straight draw (an open-ended or DBB straight draw); or, for flopping a big draw - the four flush **and** the six outs straight draw, or, the four flush **and** an inside straight draw. Of course, any flushes which you make with these suited connectors of maximum stretch will not be the nuts, except for that rare bird, the straight flush. If you are drawing to a flush, and your intuition tells you that one or more players are also on a flush draw, the chances of completion go down (fewer flush cards are left in the deck), as well as your confidence that you have a draw, which if completed, will win the money. As far as straights are concerned, you can know when you have the nuts and at worst will split the pot. You can also know when it is possible to lose to a higher straight, or better hand if the board has paired and/or a flush is possible. Again, your intuition must guide you as to whether to continue with the hand or fold. Good intuition is one of the most important traits of a winning player. Some final points and caveats before we get to the work at hand. Because suited connectors have flush and straight potential, it is possible to overquantify that potential, and make this starting hand seem stronger than it really is. To guard against this, we will have to employ a **rigorous** methodology to ensure that we do not double, or even triple count combinations. For example, after we have determined the number of **all** the combinations which will flop a straight to our starting hand, we have to be sure to not count any more straight making combinations when looking at situations such as determining the number of combinations which flop a four flush or an open-ended straight. The same caveat applies to those combinations which flop the flush. If we succeed in doing this, we will be able to **accurately** portray the probabilities of suited connectors, and produce a record as a permanent reference. A note: an eight outs straight draw is either an open-ended or a DBB straight draw. Lastly, in addition to the flush and straight making potential of suited connectors, there is also the potential to make one pair, two pair, etc., just like **any** starting hand of two different ranks. For those probabilities see the annex, **OFFSUIT CARDS**.

MAX STRETCH CONNECTORS

In the annex, **CONNECTORS**, it was determined that there were **seven** two card connectors with maximum stretch: 45, 56, 67, 78, 89, 9T, and TJ. Each of these connector combinations can flop **four** different straights, **three** open-ended and **two** DBB straight **draws**. For each connector, 78 for example, there are 8*7/2*1-6-6= 16, sixteen 78 combinations, **four** of which are suited. In total, there are only 7*4= **28** suited and sequenced connectors of maximum stretch. That makes them as rare as the total number of AA, KK, and AK combinations (8*7/2*1= 28). You can expect to receive them as a starting hand 28/1326= **2.1%** of the time.

FLOPPING A FLUSH OR STRAIGHT

FLOPPING A FLUSH
Holding JT of clubs as your starting hand, there are 11 flush cards remaining with which to make a flush. The **total** number of three card flush combinations which can be made from 11 cards is 11*10*9/3*2*1= **165**.

The probability of flopping a flush is 165/19600= .0084= **.84%**.

FLOPPING A STRAIGHT

Looking again at JT of clubs as our example, the straight can be made on the flop with 789, 89Q, 9QK, and KQA. Looking only at 789 for the moment, for all the 7s, 8s, and 9s, there are sixty-four 789 combinations which will make a straight (see the chapter, **REFERENCE COMBINATIONS**, for how this is derived). One of those combinations, 789 of clubs, will make the straight flush and has already been counted in the flush section of the previous page, leaving **63** combinations which make a straight that is beaten by any flush. The same holds true for 89Q, 9QK, and KQA. When holding JT of clubs in your hand, the total possible number of flops with the 50 remaining cards is 50*49*48/3*2*1= 19600, and the probability of flopping one of the four possible straights is 4*63/19600= 252/19600= .01296= **1.3%**.

SUMMARY OF FLUSH AND STRAIGHT

The probability of flopping **either** a flush **or** a straight when holding JT of clubs is (165+252)/19600= 417/19600= **2.13%**.
The same will be true for any other suited connector of maximum stretch. **Remember**, all the straight and flush making combinations for the flop have now been counted. In the work to come, we do not want to include these combinations. If we did, we would overstate their probability. We shall see.

A FOUR FLUSH OR EIGHT OUTS STRAIGHT DRAW

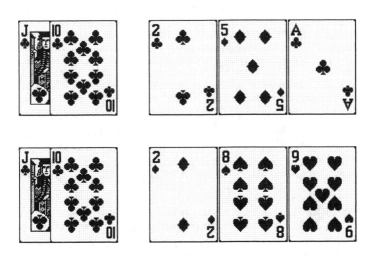

It is more probable that we will flop **either** a four flush **or** an open-ended straight draw, and we will derive the numbers to prove it. We can also flop a DBB straight draw. Not surprisingly, doing this **correctly** requires more work and more thought. The case of flopping a four flush **and** a six outs straight draw, or a four flush **and** an inside straight draw is dealt with in its own section, but we will determine the numbers of those combinations in **this** section and **subtract** those numbers to arrive at the number of combinations which flop **only** a four flush. Those subtracted numbers of combinations appear in later sections- they are not forgotten. Remember, our goal in this section is to determine the number of combinations that result in only a four flush **or** an eight outs straight draw, and to avoid doing any double counting of combinations.

FLOPPING A FOUR FLUSH

Again, assume that we are holding JT of clubs. In this section, we want to determine the probability of flopping **only** a four flush (those combinations could also pair us or put a pair on board) and **no other hand or draw**. I specify this requirement, not because of an obsession with a bare bones flush draw, but for two very good reasons: some of the two club combinations will produce a straight, and those combinations have already been counted; and secondly, some of those two club combinations produce a four flush **and** straight draws which we will isolate and deal with in their own section. In this manner, we can arrive at an overall determination of the potential and strength of suited connectors. We will isolate these combinations in **four steps.** Getting the exact numbers for this involves a long and tedious process, and, in the end, may not affect your play. So, if you want to skip this next part, the results will be summarized in the tables at the end of the annex. But, if you want a mental workout, hang in.

In this **first step**, we will remove those 'two club', three card combinations which produce a straight when holding JT of clubs. With 11 clubs remaining, the number of two club combinations is $11*10/2*1 = 55$, and each of those combinations can combine with a third card as long as it is **not** a club and

156

does **not** produce a straight. It would be a straightforward matter of multiplying those 55 combinations by the 39 remaining non-club cards to get a total of 55*39= 2145 two club, three card flops, were it not for the condition we imposed of **not** flopping a straight. In order to solve this problem, we will have to look at those **specific** two card flush combinations where a third card could make a straight. For example, with 78 of clubs on the flop, any of the three 9s which are not a club would make a straight. The two card, two club combinations presenting the same dilemma are **79** with the 8s, **89** with the 7s and Qs, **8Q** with the 9s, **9Q** with the 8s and Ks, **9K** with the Qs, **QK** with the 9s and As, **QA** with the Ks, and **KA** with the Qs. There are nine troublesome two club combinations in all. Therefore, these nine two card, two club combinations can have fewer cards as their third card. We must determine the cards with which they can combine.

For 89, there are six cards which could make a straight, the three 7s and the three Qs which are not clubs. Note that **all** three club combinations have already been accounted for. The six card problem is also true for 9Q, and QK. The two club combinations of 78, 79, 8Q, 9K, QA, and KA, are each three card problems, i.e., the trouble cards would have to come on the inside.

The number of three card combinations which the 89 of clubs can make without producing a straight is 48-6-9= **33** (the six represents the three 7s and the three Qs, the nine represents the remaining clubs). For the three combinations affected in this

157

way, the number of two club combinations which do not make a straight is 3*33= **99**.

The number of three card combinations which the 79 of clubs can make without producing a straight is 48-3-9= **36** (the three represents the three non-club 8s, the nine represents the remaining clubs). For the six combinations affected in this way, the number of four flush combinations is 6*36= **216**. That was tough. The next part is easy.

Now for the rest of the two club combinations. For the other two card, two club combinations which require no reduction, i.e., 55-9= 46, each may combine with the 48-9= 39 non-club cards, giving 46*39= 1794 combinations.

The total number of two club, non-straightening combinations is 99+216+1794= **2109**. That makes the number of two club **straight making** combinations equal to 2145-2109= **36**. Those 36 combinations have already been included in the previous section as part of the 252 combinations which can flop a straight to JT. We have now removed those three card combinations which contain two clubs and would make a straight for a starting hand of JT of clubs, and are one step closer to determining the number of combinations which flop only a four flush.

Now for **step two.** Buried in those **2109** two club, non-straightening, three card combinations, are a number of combinations which produce the monster draw of a four flush **and** an open-ended straight draw of six outs. These draws have a total of 15 outs to make the straight **or** flush, so we'd like to know how many of them there are. Also in there, are a number of combinations which give the four flush **and** a DBB straight draw of six outs, also for a total of 15 outs to make the straight **or** flush, but we will determine those numbers in **step three**. Last and least, there are also the combinations which will flop a four flush **and** an inside straight draw, with twelve outs to complete a hand. We will determine those numbers in **step four**. If we can determine these numbers, we will be able to produce a permanent and **accurate** table on the drawing power of suited connectors.

For **step two**, we want to determine the number of combinations producing the flush draw **and** open-ended straight draw for the JT of clubs. There are three situations which will produce the open-ended straight draw: **x89** (x cannot be a 7 or Q), **x9Q** (x cannot be an 8 or K), and **xQK** (x cannot be a 9 or an A). Once again, those two club combinations which flop a straight have already been accounted for. A further requirement for the combinations is that, two, and only two, of the cards **must be** clubs. Alas, I do not know of an easy and quick way to solve this.

For the case of x89, there are three, **two club**, models- a) Xdhs8c9c, b) Xc8c9dhs, and c) Xc8dhs9c. X, 8, and 9 are in the suit or suits indicated. Looking at a) first, x can be any diamond, heart, or spade of the ranks 2, 3, 4, 5, 6, 8, 9, T, J, K, and A. All the 7s and Qs are excluded because they would make straights. Therefore, x can be any of 3*11= 33 cards, making 33 combinations of the a) model. Note that some of these combinations produce a pair on board, as will be true of the other models.

For model b), Xc8c9dhs, x **must be** a club. Those clubs fitting the criteria and which are available are 2, 3, 4, 5, 6, K, and A, seven in all. Either of these clubs, along with the 8 of clubs, may combine with either the 9 of diamonds, hearts, or spades, resulting in 7*3= 21 combinations. Model c), Xc8dhs9c, has the same structure as model b) and therefore, 21 combinations as well.

Summarizing, the number of two club combinations which produce a four flush **and** an x89 open-ended straight draw for JT of clubs is 33+2*21= 33+42= 75. The same is true for x9Q and xQK. The number of two club combinations which produce a four flush **and** an open-ended straight draw is 3*75= **225**.

For step **three**, we want to determine the number of combinations which produce the flush draw **and** the DBB straight draw. The DBB straight draws for TJ are 79K and 8QA. Each draw can make 3*2/2*1= 3 two club combinations. Each two club combination can combine with the three other suits of the other rank, giving 3*3= 9 DBB combinations of two clubs. The total number of combinations for the two draws is 2*9= **18**.

For the straight draws, the number of two club combinations which produce a four flush and a **six** outs straight draw (with the flush draw, two of the straight draws eight outs are clubs and contribute to making the flush leaving only six outs) is 225+18= **243**.

For **step four**, we want to determine the number of combinations producing the flush draw **and** inside straight draw for the JT of clubs. There are six situations which will produce the inside straight draw: 7x9, 78x, 8xQ, 9xK, xKA, and QxA. X cannot be the rank which makes the straight in the specific situation. A further requirement for the combinations is that, two, and only two, of the cards must be clubs. Not easy, but the methodology is the same as in step two.

For the situation of xKA, there are three, **two club**, models- a) XdhsKcAc, b) XcKcAdhs, and c) XcKdhsAc. X, K, and A are in the suit or suits indicated. Looking at a) first, x can be any diamond, heart, or spade of the ranks 2, 3, 4, 5, 6, 7, 8, 9, T, J, K, and A. The three Qs are excluded because they make the straight. Therefore, x can be any of the 3*12= 36 cards, making 36 combinations of the a) model. Note that some of these combinations produce a pair on board, as will be true of the other models.

For model b), XcKcAdhs, **x must be** a club. Those clubs fitting the criteria and which are available are 2, 3, 4, 5, 6, 7, 8, and 9, eight in all. Either of these clubs, along with the King of clubs, may combine with either the Ace of diamonds, hearts, or spades, resulting in 8*3= 24 combinations. Model c), XcKdhsAc, has the same structure as model b) and therefore, 24 combinations.

Summarizing, the number of two club combinations which produce a four flush and a xKA inside straight draw for JT of clubs is 36+2*24= 36+48= 84. The same is true for the other five situations. The number of two club combinations which produce a four flush **and** an inside straight draw are 6*84= **504**.

At last we can sum up and make some comments. The number of two club, three card flop combinations which produce a four flush and **not** a straight, **nor** a four flush **and** six outs straight draw, **nor** a four flush **and** three outs straight draw is 2145-36-243-504= **1362**. You will flop this sanitized four flush 1362/19600= **7%** of the time. We also can begin to see why suited connectors are potentially so powerful. Of the 2145 possible four flush combinations, 1362, or 63% of them produce only a four flush, but a significant 2145-1362= 783 combinations, or **37%** of them produce either a straight, or a four flush **and** a straight draw.

FLOPPING AN OPEN-ENDED STRAIGHT DRAW

Again, using JT of clubs as our starting cards, we want to determine the number of flop combinations which result in a purely open-ended straight draw.

The open-ended straight draw can be made with a flop of **x89**, **x9Q**, and **xQK** (three open-ended straight draws), where x cannot be a card which makes the straight. Those combinations have already been counted. Also, the flop cannot contain two or three clubs, because that would mean we had flopped a flush, or a four flush. Here we are looking for the three card combinations which produce **only** an open-ended straight draw.

Looking at the case of x89: the number of 89 combinations which can be made from the four 8s and four 9s is the same as for AK- there are 16, one of which is the 89 of clubs, which we'll drop from consideration right now, because it would flop us a four flush, and is a combination which was previously accounted for. That leaves us fifteen 89 combinations. X is any of the remaining cards but cannot be a 7 or a Q, because those two ranks would make a straight, and straight making combinations have already been accounted for. Therefore, x equals 48 (you hold JT and the flop is x89) minus four 7s and four Qs giving 40 cards. The number of x89 combinations is 15*40= 600 **less** the number of those x89 combinations which contain two clubs and have previously been accounted for. The x89 combinations which contain two clubs are models b and c from the previous section in step two. Each of the two x89 combinations meeting the criteria have 21 combinations which contain two clubs. Therefore, the number of x89 combinations which produce an open-ended straight only is 600-42= **558**. The same holds true for the other two possibilities, so that we have 3*558= **1674** combinations which will give an open-ended straight draw only. Therefore, the probability of flopping an open-ended straight draw is 1674/19600= .085= **8.5%**.

Note that if we had JT offsuit, the number of combinations which would give an open-ended straight is 640 (see, **CONNECTORS**). If we look at our 558 combinations and now add back the 42 three card combinations containing two clubs, and add the number of three card combinations containing 89 of clubs (89 of clubs may combine with any of the 40 remaining non-straightening cards), then we have a total of 558+42+40= 640.

FLOPPING A DBB STRAIGHT DRAW

I have included the DBB straight draw because if you flop one, you have eight outs, just like an open-ended straight draw; you also have a well-disguised drawing hand. In order to flop a DBB straight draw, all three cards must fit, just like a straight. It should come as no surprise that the probability of flopping a particular DBB straight draw is the same as flopping a particular straight. For JT of clubs, there are two DBB straight draws: 79K (an 8 or a Q make the straight) and 8QA (a 9 or a K make the straight). The number of 79K sequences which can be made from all the 7s, 9s, and Ks is 64 (see, **REFERENCE COMBINATIONS**, for how this is derived). One of those 64 combinations is the 79K of clubs which would make a flush on the flop and has already been accounted for, therefore, there are 63 DBB straight draw combinations for 79K. The same is true for 8QA. But again, we must strip out those combinations which contain two clubs, because they have already been accounted for. In the previous section in step 3, we determined that the number of combinations which contained two clubs for each of the draws was nine, so that the total number of 79K and 8QA combinations containing two clubs is 2*9=18. The total number of combinations which give a DBB straight draw **and** not a four flush draw is 2*63-18= 126-18= **108**. The probability of flopping a DBB straight draw is 108/19600= .55%

Summary of straight draws

The probability of hitting an open-ended or DBB straight draw with a max stretch suited connector is (1674+108)/19600= 1782/19600= **9.1%**

SUMMARY OF FLUSH AND STRAIGHT DRAWS

The probability of flopping either a flush draw **or** an eight outs straight draw, but not the straight, and not the flush **and** straight draws, when holding suited connectors of maximum stretch is

(1362+1782)/19600= 3144/19600= **16%**. If you are able to flop **one** of these draws, the probability of completion is as follows: for the case of flopping the four flush, the probability of hitting one or two more flush cards with your nine out draw and two cards to come is 35%, or odds against of 1.9:1; for the case of an eight outs straight draw (the open-ended and DBB straight draws), the probability of hitting one or two of your outs is 31.5%, or odds against of 2.2:1. The numbers for the probabilities and odds are taken from, **TABLE OF TWO TO COME**.

FLOPPING BOTH DRAWS

A FOUR FLUSH AND SIX OUTS STRAIGHT DRAW
Depicted below are two examples of flopping **both** a four flush **and** a six outs straight draw.

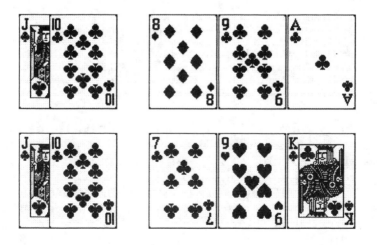

The probability of flopping the **monster**, i.e., **both** a four flush **and** a six outs straight draw, was determined in the section on flopping a four flush (see steps two and three) and is (225+18)/19600= 243/19600= 1.24%, or odds against of **80:1**. Not very likely. **But**, if you do flop this monster, this draw has 15 outs (nine flush cards and the six remaining straight cards) and a probability to hit either one or two outs of **54.1%**, or odds against of **.85:1**, with two cards to come (see **TABLE OF TWO TO COME**). You're a favorite to complete the hand! Note that if you do complete this monster, be aware that there are many other hands which you could lose to. Poker is a tough game with few guarantees.

A FLUSH DRAW AND THREE OUTS STRAIGHT DRAW

Depicted below is an example of flopping **both** a four flush **and** a three outs inside straight draw.

The probability of flopping the **elephant**, i.e., **both** a four flush **and** a three outs inside straight draw, was determined in step four in the section on flopping a four flush and is 504/19600= **2.6%**, or odds against of **38:1**. Not bad. If you do flop this elephant, this draw has 12 outs (nine flush cards and the three remaining inside straight cards)

and a probability to hit either one or two outs of **45%**, or odds against of **1.2:1**, with two cards to come (see **TABLE OF TWO TO COME**). You're almost a favorite to complete the hand! Note that if you do bag this elephant, be aware that there are many other hands which you could lose to.

ONE-GAP SUITED CONNECTORS

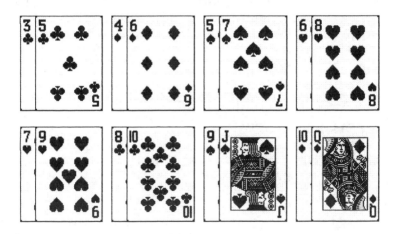

In late position with many callers and in an unraised pot, one-gap connectors such as the following are often profitably (or are perceived to be) played: 35, 46, 57, 68, 79, 8T, 9J, and of course TQ. All these connectors can flop a maximum of **three** straights. The connectors 57, 68, 79, and 8T can flop **three** DBB straight **draws.** The connectors 35, 46, 9J, and TQ can flop **two**

DBB straight **draws.** For the one-gap connector 8T, there are sixteen 8T combinations, four of which are suited. The same is true for each of the other connectors. The total number of max stretch, one-gap suited connectors is 8*4=32. You can expect to receive one of these suited connectors as your starting hand 32/1326= **2.4%** of the time. What we did for suited sequenced connectors, we will now do for suited one-gap connectors. For this example we will use 8T of clubs. All the same caveats and comments on methodology mentioned for sequenced connectors apply here as well. For the pair, two pair, etc., possibilities of these hands, see the annex, **OFFSUIT CARDS.**

FLOPPING A FLUSH OR A STRAIGHT

FLOPPING A FLUSH
The probability of flopping a flush when holding 8T of clubs is the same as for any two suited cards- **.84%.**

FLOPPING A STRAIGHT
Taking 8T of clubs as our example, the number of straights which can be flopped is three; 6789T, 789TJ, and 89TJQ. For each three card sequence giving a straight (679, 79J, and 9JQ), there are 64 combinations, one of which makes a straight flush and has already been counted in the flush section above, leaving 63 straight making combinations. Therefore, the probability of flopping a straight is 3*63/19600= 189/19600= .0096= 1%. Note that by playing a one gap hand, we can flop only three

straights as opposed to four for JT.

SUMMARY OF FLUSH AND STRAIGHT

The probability of flopping **either** a flush **or** a straight with a suited, one-gap connector of maximum stretch is (165+189)/19600= 354/19600= **1.8%**

A FOUR FLUSH OR EIGHT OUTS STRAIGHT DRAW

Again, assume that we are holding 8T of clubs. In this section, we want to determine the probability of flopping **only** a four flush (those combinations could also pair us or put a pair on board) and **no other hand or draw**. I specify this requirement, not because of an obsession with a bare bones flush draw, but for two very good reasons: some of the two club combinations will produce a straight, and those combinations have already been counted; and secondly, some of those two club combinations produce a four flush **and** straight draws which we will isolate and deal with in their own section. In this manner, we can arrive at an overall determination of the potential and strength of suited connectors. We will isolate these combinations in **four steps**.

In this **first step**, we will remove those 'two club', three card combinations which produce a straight when holding 8T of clubs. With 11 clubs remaining, the number of two club combinations is 11*10/2*1= 55, and each of those combinations can combine with a third card as long as it is **not** a club and does **not** produce a straight. It would be a straightforward matter of multiplying those 55 combinations by the 39 remaining non-club cards to get a total of 55*39= 2145 two club, three card flops, were it not for the condition we imposed of **not** flopping a straight. In order to solve this problem, we will have to look at those **specific** two card flush combinations where a third card could make a straight. For example, with 69 of clubs on the flop, any of the three 7s which are not a club would make a straight. The two card, two club combinations presenting the same dilemma are **67** with the 9s, **79** with the 6s and Js, **7J** with the 9s, **9J** with the 7s and Qs, **9Q** with the Js, and **JQ** with the 9s. There are seven troublesome two club combinations in all. Therefore, these seven 'two card', two club combinations can have fewer cards as their third card. We must determine the cards with which they can combine.

For 79, there are six cards which could make a straight, the three 6s and the three Js, which are not clubs. Note that **all** three club combinations have already been accounted for. The six card problem is also true for 9J. The two club combinations of 67, 69, 7J, 9Q, and JQ are each three card problems, i.e., the trouble cards would have to come on the inside.

The number of three card combinations which the 79 of clubs can make without producing a straight is 48-6-9= **33** (the six represents the three 6s and the three Js, the nine represents the remaining clubs). For the two combinations affected in this way, the number of two club combinations which do not make a straight is 2*33= **66**.

The number of three card combinations which the 69 of clubs can make without producing a straight is 48-3-9= 36 (the three represents the three non-club 7s, the nine represents the remaining clubs). For the five combinations affected in this way, the number of four flush combinations is 5*36= **180**. That was tough. The next part is easy.

Now for the rest of the two club combinations. For the other two card, two club combinations which require no reduction, i.e., 55-7= 48, each may combine with the 48-9= 39 non-club cards, giving 48*39= 1872 combinations.

The total number of two club, non-straightening combinations is 66+180+1872= **2118**. That makes the number of two club **straight making** combinations equal to 2145-2118= **27**. Those 27 combinations have already been included in the previous section as part of the 189 combinations which can flop a straight to 8T. We have now removed those three card combinations which contain two clubs and would make a straight for a starting hand of 8T of clubs, and are one step closer to determining the number of combinations which flop only a four flush.

Now for **step two**. Buried in those **2118** two club, non-straightening, three card combinations, are a number of combinations which produce the monster draw of a four flush **and** an open-ended straight draw of six outs. These draws have a total of 15 outs to make the straight **or** flush, so we'd like to know how many of them there are. Also in there, are a number of combinations which give the four flush **and** a DBB straight draw of six outs, also for a total of 15 outs to make the straight **or** flush, but we will determine those numbers in **step three**. Last and least, there are also the combinations which will flop a four flush **and** an inside straight draw, with twelve outs to complete a hand. We will determine those numbers in **step four**. If we can determine these numbers, we will be able to produce a permanent and **accurate** table on the drawing power of suited one-gap connectors.

For **step two**, we want to determine the number of combinations producing the flush draw **and** open-ended straight draw for the 8T of clubs. There are two situations which will produce the open-ended straight draw: **x79** (x cannot be a 6 or J), and **x9J** (x cannot be a 7 or Q). Once again, those two club combinations which flop a straight have already been accounted for. A further requirement for the combinations is that, two, and only two, of the cards **must be** clubs. Alas, I do not know of an easy and quick way to solve this.

For the case of x79, there are three, **two club**, models- a) Xdhs7c9c, b) Xc7c9dhs, and c) Xc7dhs9c. X, 7, and 9 are in the suit or suits indicated. Looking at a) first, x can be any diamond, heart, or spade of the ranks 2, 3, 4, 5, 7, 8, 9, T, Q, K, and A. All the 6s and Js are excluded because they would make straights. Therefore, x can be any of 3*11= 33 cards, making 33 combinations of the a) model. Note that some of these combinations produce a pair on board, as will be true of the other models.

For model b), Xc7c9dhs, x **must be** a club. Those clubs fitting the criteria and which are available are 2, 3, 4, 5, Q, K, and A, seven in all. Either of these clubs along with the 7 of clubs, may combine with either the 9 of diamonds, hearts, or spades, resulting in 7*3= 21 combinations. Model c), Xc7dhs9c, has the same structure as model b) and therefore, 21 combinations as well.

Summarizing, the number of two club combinations which produce a four flush and an x79 open-ended straight draw for 8T of clubs is 33+2*21= 33+42= 75. The same is true for x9J. The number of two club combinations which produce a four flush and an open-ended straight draw are 2*75= 150.

For step **three**, we want to determine the number of combinations which produce the flush draw and the DBB straight draw. For 8T there are **three** DBB straight draws. For JT there were only two. The DBB straight draws for 8T are 467, 69Q, and JQA. Each draw can make 3*2/2*1= 3 two club combinations. Each two club combination can combine with the three other suits of the other rank, giving 3*3= 9 DBB combinations of two clubs. The total number of combinations for the three draws is 3*9= 27.

For the straight draws, the number of two club combinations which produce a four flush and a **six** outs straight draw (with the flush draw, two of the straight draws eight outs are clubs and contribute to making the flush leaving only six outs) is 150+27= **177**.

For **step four**, we want to determine the number of combinations producing the flush draw **and** inside straight draw for the 8T of clubs. There are four situations which will produce the inside straight draw: 67x, 7xJ, xJQ, and 9xQ. X cannot be the rank which makes the straight in the specific situation. A further requirement for the combinations is that, two, and only two, of the cards must be clubs. Again, no easy way, but the methodology is the same as in step two.

For the situation of xJQ, there are

three, **two club**, models- a) XdhsJcQc, b) XcJcQdhs, and c) XcJdhsQc. X, J, and Q are in the suit or suits indicated. Looking at a) first, x can be any diamond, heart, or spade of the ranks 2, 3, 4, 5, 6, 7, 8, T, J, Q, K, and A. The three 9s are excluded because they make the straight. Therefore, x can be any of the 3*12= 36 cards, making 36 combinations of the a) model. Note that some of these combinations produce a pair on board, as will be true of the other models.

For model b), XcJcQdhs, x **must be** a club. Those clubs fitting the criteria and which are available are 2, 3, 4, 5, 6, 7, K, and A, eight in all. Either of these clubs along with the Jack of clubs, may combine with either the Queen of diamonds, hearts, or spades, resulting in 8*3= 24 combinations. Model c), XcJdhsQc, has the same structure as model b) and therefore, 24 combinations.

Summarizing, the number of two club combinations which produce a four flush and a xJQ inside straight draw for 8T of clubs is 36+2*24= 36+48= 84. The same is true for the other three situations. The number of two club combinations which produce a four flush **and** an inside straight draw are 4*84= **336**.

At last we can sum up and make some comments. The number of two club, three card flop combinations which produce a four flush and **not** a straight, **nor** a four flush **and** six outs straight draw, **nor** a four flush **and** three outs straight draw is 2145-27-177-336= **1605** when holding a suited one-gap connector of maximum stretch. You will flop this sanitized four flush 1605/19600= **8.2%** of the time. We also can begin to see why suited connectors are potentially so powerful. Of the 2145 possible four flush combinations, 1605, or, 75% of them produce only a four flush, but a significant 2145-1605= 540 combinations, or 25% of them produce either a straight, or a four flush **and** a straight draw. The figure for JT of clubs was 37%, or 12% greater than 8T. That's the advantage of the sequenced connector over the one-gap connector.

FLOPPING AN OPEN-ENDED STRAIGHT DRAW

There are two open-ended straight draws which can be flopped: x789T and x89TJ. The same methodology and numbers as used for JT of clubs also apply to 8T of clubs, except that there are only two open-ended straight draws as opposed to three. There are 558 open-ended straight draw making combinations which contain one club or fewer, for each draw. Therefore, the probability of flopping an open-ended straight draw is 2*558/19600= 1116/19600= .057= **5.7%**.

FLOPPING A DBB STRAIGHT DRAW

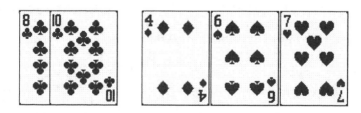

Oddly, by playing the one gap connector, we do **gain** in the number of DBB straight draws. For 8T there are three; 467, 69Q, and JQA. For TJ there were only two. For each three card sequence, there are 64 combinations, one of which will give a flush, leaving 63 which will give a DBB straight draw. But again, we must strip out those combinations which contain two clubs. Using 467 as an example, the three clubs can make 3*2/2*1= 3 two club combinations. Each combination may combine with only the remaining rank in diamonds, hearts, and spades. Therefore, there are 3*3= 9 two club combinations. The same is true for 69Q and JQA. Therefore, the total number of DBB straight draw flops containing two clubs is 3*9= 27. The total number of combinations which give a DBB straight draw **and** not a four flush draw is 3*63-27= 189-27= 162. The probability of flopping a DBB straight draw is 162/19600= .0083= **.8%**.

Summary of straight draws
   The probability of hitting an open-ended or DBB straight draw is (1116+162)/19600= 1278/19600= **6.5%**.

SUMMARY OF FLUSH AND STRAIGHT DRAWS
   The probability of flopping **either** a four flush **or** an eight outs straight draw, but not the straight, and not the flush **and** straight draws when holding one-gap suited connectors of maximum stretch is (1605+1278)/19600= 2883/19600= **14.7%**. If you are able to flop one of these draws, the probability of completing is as follows: for the case of flopping the four flush, the probability of hitting one or two more flush cards with your nine outs draw and two cards to come is 35%, or odds against of 1.9:1; for the case of an eight outs straight draw (the open-ended and DBB straight draws), the

176

probability of completing by hitting one or two of your outs is 31.5%, or odds against of 2.2:1, with two cards to come. The numbers for the probabilities and odds are taken from, **TABLE OF TWO TO COME.**

FLOPPING BOTH DRAWS

A FOUR FLUSH AND SIX OUTS STRAIGHT DRAW
Depicted below are two examples of flopping **both** a four flush **and** a six outs straight draw.

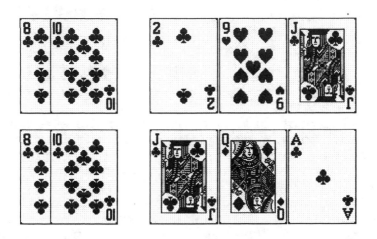

The probability of flopping the **monster**, i.e., **both** a four flush **and** a six outs straight draw, was determined in the section on flopping a four flush (see steps two and three) and is (150+27)/19600= 177/19600= .9%, or odds against of **110:1**. Not very likely. **But**, if you do flop this monster, this draw has **15** outs (nine flush cards and the six remaining straight cards) and a probability to hit either one or two outs of **54.1%**, or odds against of **.85:1**, with two cards to come (see **TABLE OF TWO TO COME**). You're a favorite to complete the hand! Note that if you do complete this monster, be aware that there are many other hands which you could lose to. Poker is a tough game with few guarantees.

A FLUSH DRAW AND THREE OUTS STRAIGHT DRAW

Depicted below is an example of flopping **both** a four flush **and** a three outs inside straight draw.

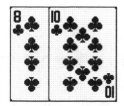 

The probability of flopping the **elephant**, i.e., **both** a four flush **and** a three outs inside straight draw, was determined in step four in the section on flopping a four flush and is 336/19600= **1.7%**, or odds against of **57:1**. Not great. If you do flop this elephant, this draw has **12** outs (nine flush cards and the three remaining inside straight cards) and a probability to hit either one or two outs of **45%**, or odds against of **1.2:1**, with two cards to come (see **TABLE OF TWO TO COME**). You're almost a favorite to complete the hand! Note that if you do bag this elephant, be aware that there are many other hands which you could lose to, as was the case for JT of clubs. For one-gap connectors such as 24 and KJ, the number of straights which can be flopped is two. Taking that into account, use the same methodology to arrive at the numbers. Note that by playing one-gap connectors you give up a few percentage points of probability. See the following two tables for comparison purposes.

CONCLUSIONS

Suited connectors of maximum stretch, sequenced and one-gap, have high probabilities of flopping a hand or a draw relative to **offsuit** connectors, with a particularly high probability of completion where the straight **and** flush draws are flopped. **But,** having said that, let me add this sobering example. If you look down and see that you were dealt JT suited as your starting hand, the probability of being dealt the monster, i.e., **both** a four flush **and** a six outs straight draw, is 243/19600= .012= 1.2%. The probability of then making either a flush or a straight is 595/1081= .541= 54.1%. The combined probability of getting this flop and completing the hand is the product of the probabilities, i.e., 243/19600*595/1081= .0068= **.68%,** less than 1%. Hope and reality tend to diverge in Hold'em poker, and a big pocket pair is kind of comforting. The preceding material is tabulated in the two following appendices.

Final Note: I have not dealt with any exotic hands such as flopping a straight flush when holding JT of clubs. For those with stars in their eyes, there are four combinations which flop straight flushes: 789, 89Q, 9QK, and QKA of clubs. The probability of flopping a straight flush is 4/19600= .0002= .02%. The odds against it are **4899:1.**

TABLE OF SEQUENCED SUITED CONNECTORS*

	# combos	%	Odds
To get max connector, suited and no-gap, as hole cards	28/1326	2.1	46:1
For any of the seven, the probability of flopping:			
a flush	165/19600	.84	118:1
a straight (4 possible)	252/ @	1.3	77:1
a straight or flush	417/ @	2.1	46:1
a four flush**	2145/19600	11	8:1
a four flush***	2109/ @	10.8	8:1
a four flush****	1362/ @	7	13:1
open-ended straight draw	1674/ @	8.5	11:1
a DBB straight draw	108/ @	.55	180:1
open-ended or DBB str draw	1782/ @	9	10:1
four flush^ or 8 outs str dr	3144/ @	16	5:1
four flush and 6 outs str dr	243/ @	1.2	80:1
four flush and 3 outs str dr	504/ @	2.6	38:1
four flush and any str draw	747/ @	3.8	25:1
Probability of completing with two cards to come:			
the flush draw	378/1081	35	1.9:1
8 outs straight draw	340/ @	31.5	2.2:1
four flush and 6 outs str dr	595/ @	54.1	.85:1
four flush and 3 outs str dr	486/ @	45	1.2:1

* For the group of seven: 45, 56, 67, 78, 89, 9T, TJ.
** Includes those combinations which flop a straight and those combinations which flop both a four flush and straight draws, i.e., a four flush.
*** Excludes those combos which flop a straight, but includes those combos which flop both a four flush and straight draws (six and three outs).
**** A four flush without the straight making combos, and those combos which flop both a four flush and straight draws (six and three outs).
^ the four flush is as described at ****
Note: 78 suited vs 78 offsuit is in, DISCUSSION, in annex, SUITED CARDS.

TABLE OF ONE-GAP SUITED CONNECTORS*

	# combos	%	Odds
To get max connector, suited and one-gap, as hole cards	32/1326	2.4	40:1
For any of the eight, the probability of flopping:			
a flush	165/19600	.84	118:1
a straight (3 possible)	189/ @	1	103:1
a straight or flush	354/ @	1.8	54:1
a four flush**	2145/19600	11	8:1
a four flush***	2118/ @	10.8	8:1
a four flush****	1605/ @	8.2	11:1
open-ended straight draw	1116/ @	5.7	17:1
a DBB straight draw (3)#	162/ @	.8	120:1
open-ended or DBB str draw	1278/ @	6.5	14:1
four flush^ or 8 outs str dr	2883/ @	15	5.8:1
four flush and 6 outs str dr	177/ @	.9	110:1
four flush and 3 outs str dr	336/ @	1.7	57:1
four flush and any str draw	513/ @	2.6	37:1
Probability of completing with two cards to come:			
the flush draw	378/1081	35	1.9:1
8 outs straight draw	340/ @	31.5	2.2:1
four flush and 6 outs str dr	595/ @	54.1	.85:1
four flush and 3 outs str dr	486/ @	45	1.2:1

* For the group of eight: 35, 46, 57, 68, 79, 8T, 9J, and TQ.
** Includes those combinations which flop a straight and those combinations which flop both a four flush and straight draws, i.e., a four flush.
*** Excludes those combos which flop a straight, but includes those combos which flop both a four flush and straight draws (six and three outs).
**** A four flush without the straight making combos, and those combos which flop both a four flush and straight draws (six and three outs).
^ the four flush is as described at ****
# 57:A34, 369, 89J/68:245, 47T, 9TQ/79:356, 58J, TJK/8T:467, 69Q, and JQA
Note: 35, 46, 9J and TQ have only two DBB straight draws and each can flop 108/19600 combinations, with a probability of .55%.

HAND RANKINGS

The hands in poker are ranked according to their rarity in five cards, and that is the first thing a new player learns: a straight flush beats quads, quads beat a full house, all the way down to a pair beating no pair. **Although Hold'em is a seven card game, the hands are ranked as if it was a five card game.** The two extra cards increase the probability of making hands and make for a lot more action, but result in some contradictions which will be discussed in a later section. Back to reality and the work at hand. The total number of five card poker hands which can be made from 52 cards is 52*51*50*49*48/5*4*3*2*1= **2,598,960**. That number encompasses all the straight flushes, all the quads, all the full houses, all the flushes, all the straights, all the trips, all the two pairs, all the pair and non-pair combinations. When your hand is shown down at the river, you will show one of those **2,598,960** hands.

STRAIGHT FLUSHES

To determine the number of straight flushes for one suit, lay out the cards of that suit sequentially from deuce to Ace. Grab another Ace and pretend it is the same suit as the cards just laid out and put it to the left of the deuce. Start from left to right and count the number of five card straight flushes: Ace to 5, 2 to 6, etc.- 10 straight flushes in all. For the four suits, the number of straight flushes is 4*10= **40**.

QUADS

To determine the number of quads, grab the four deuces. The four deuces may have as its fifth card any of the remaining 48 cards. That makes 48 hands of quad deuces. The same will be true for any other rank. Therefore, there are 13*48= **624** hands of quads.

FULL HOUSES

To determine the number of full houses, grab the Aces. The model for full houses is xxxyy, where xxx is a three of a kind combination, and yy is any other pair. The four Aces can make 4*3*2/3*2*1= 4 three of a kind combinations. Each of the other 12 ranks can make 4*3/2*1= 6 pair combinations, for a total of 72 pair combinations. The number of Aces full is 4*72= 288. The same will be true for any rank, therefore, there are 13*288= **3744** different full houses.

FLUSHES

To determine the number of flushes, take the 13 cards of the same suit and calculate the number of five card combinations. The number of flushes for one suit is 13*12*11*10*9/5*4*3*2*1= 154,440/120= 1287. Since 10 of those 1287 flushes are straight flushes and have already been accounted for, we have 1277 flushes for one suit that are beaten by any full house. The total number of these flushes is 1277*4= **5108**.

STRAIGHTS

In our earlier work, we determined that the total number of any type of straight was 1024. Of that number, four are straight flushes and have already been accounted for, leaving 1020 straights beaten by any flush. As with the straight flushes, there are 10 types of straights, from the bicycle to broadway. Therefore, there are **10200** straights.

TRIPS

Trips fit the model xxxyz, where yz are any two other cards that do not make a pair. The number of trips for any rank is 4*3*2/3*2*1= 24/6= 4. The remaining 48 cards can make 48*47/2*1= 2256/2= 1128 two card combinations. But that number also includes pairs, so we must subtract the number of pairs from 1128. Any rank can make six pairs. The 12 remaining ranks contain 6*12= 72 pairs. The number of yz combinations is 1128-72= 1056. For any rank, the number of trips is 4*1056= 4224. For the 13 ranks, the total number of trips is 13*4224= **54,912**.

TWO PAIRS

The model for two pairs is xxyyz. This is the most difficult hand to calculate because AAKK is exactly the same as KKAA. You'll soon see. Take Aces: there are six pairs, and they may combine with any of the other 12*6= 72 pair combinations. The number of AAyy combinations is 6*72= 432. Each of those combinations can have as its fifth card any of the remaining 44 cards. The number of AAyyz combinations is 44*432= 19008.

The number of KKyy combinations appears to be the same as for the Aces, i.e., 432, but where yy is any of the six AA combinations, we are repeating from the AAKK combinations above. The number of AAKK combinations is 6*6=36. Therefore, the number of unaccounted for KKyy combinations is 432-36= 396. Each of those combinations can have as its fifth card any of the remaining 44 cards. The number of KKyyz combinations, where yy cannot be AA is 396*44= 17424.

The model for Queens is QQyyz, where yy cannot be AA or KK, since they have already been accounted for. That excludes 36+36= 72 combinations. The number of unaccounted for QQyy combinations is 432-72= 360. With any of the remaining 44 cards for the fifth, we have 360*44= 15840.

The pattern has become obvious. As we go further down the ranks, there are 36 fewer combinations than previously, because they have been accounted for higher up the chain. The total number of two pair combinations is 432+396+360+324+288+252+216+180+144+108+72+36+0= 2808. Each of those 2808 two pair combinations can have as its fifth card any of the remaining 44 cards. The total number of two pair combinations is 2808*44= **123,552.**

ONE PAIR
    The model for a single pair is xxyzw, where xx is any pair and where yzw is drawn from the remaining 48 cards and cannot be trips or a pair. For yzw, the number of three card combinations which can be made from 48 cards is 48*47*46/3*2*1= 103776/6= 17296. From that number we must strip out the trips and pairs. The 48 remaining cards comprise 12 ranks. Each rank can form 4*3*2/3*2*1= 4 trips combinations. The total number of trips is 4*12=48. The number of

pairs possible from the remaining 12 ranks is 12*6=72. Any of those 72 pairs can combine with the remaining 44 cards. The number of three card combinations containing a pair is 72*44= 3168. The number of three card combinations containing neither trips nor a pair is 17296-48-3168= 14080. The number of single pairs is 78, and they may combine with any of the 14080 yzw combinations. The total number of single pair combinations is 78*14080= **1,098,240.**

NO PAIR
The number of no pair five card poker hands is the sum of the above hands subtracted from the total possible number of hands. The total of the above hands is 40+ 624+ 3744+ 5108+ 10200+ 54912+ 123552+ 1,098,240= 1,296,420. The number of no pair five card hands is 2,598,960- 1,296,420= **1,302,540.**

TABLE OF HAND RANKINGS

HAND	#	ODDS (in five cards)	% of hands
Straight Flushes	40	64,973:1	0.0015
Quads	624	4,164:1	0.024
Full Houses	3,744	693:1	0.144
Flushes	5,108	508:1	0.197
Straights	10,200	254:1	0.392
Trips	54,912	46:1	2.11
Two pairs	123,552	20:1	4.75
One pair	1,098,240	1.4:1	42.26
No pair	1,302,540*	1.0:1	50.12

*One half of 2,598,960 is 1,299,480. Just over half of the total possible five card poker hands are no pair. Note that a one pair hand is not that much rarer than a no pair hand.

DISCUSSION

As mentioned in the section on Hand Rankings, Hold'em is a seven card game using the hand rankings of a five card game. With seven cards, the total possible number of hands is **133,784,560**. That number is about 51 and a half times larger than the number of possibilities with five cards. The result is that hands which are rarer with seven cards, and could only exist with seven cards, are devalued by the five card ranking. Hands which are rarer and lose, and are frequently seen, are three pairs, as shown on the previous page, a no pair hand, and a low end seven card straight. My purpose in pointing out these contradictions is to fulfill my stated objective of completeness and as an interest item. Let's look at the example of no pair and see how it becomes more difficult to achieve relative to a pair as we increase the number of cards.

Before the flop, the total possible number of two card hands is 1326. Of that number, 78 are pairs and 1326-78= 1248 are non-pairs. The ratio of pairs to non-pairs is 78 to 1248, or **1:16**. At this point, the pair is a much rarer hand. With five cards, the number of pair combinations is 1,098,240 and the number of no pair combinations is 1,320,540, for a ratio of **1:1.2**! The ratio is equal with the addition of three cards. By the time we look at seven cards, the number of **one pair combinations is much greater than the number of no pair combinations**. The exact proof is a very tough slog and so I'll ask you to accept my statement intuitively. That rarer hand of no pair loses to the more common one pair hand because we use the rankings for a five card hand in a seven card game. Couldn't we compromise and say a no pair hand beats at least a pair of deuces? No way! C'est la vie. If Hold'em were a 13 card game that insisted on using the rankings for five card hands, it would be a major injustice for a pair of deuces to beat a no pair hand, because that hand could be nothing less than a 13 card straight!

TORONTO HOLD'EM

The cry goes up from the table, "**machine.....machine.**" The table comes to life as if pure oxygen had been pumped in. "**Machine.... machine,**" the cry goes out and dreams of getting even and making a bundle are born. The atmosphere is electric. In Toronto parlance, a **maniac** has arrived.

Toronto, Canada's largest and richest city, also known as Hogtown, Broadway, and San Francisco of the north, is the most multicultural city in the world. It is a tower of Babel: large minorities of Chinese, Vietnamese, Koreans, Greeks, Italians, south Asians, Philipinos, blacks, Jews, South Americans, Israelis, Arabs, Ukrainians, and the occasional Anglo-Saxon or two. Canada, with the highest number of millionaires per capita in the world, concentrates its money here. At the poker table, the dealer repeats his mantra, "English only while the hand is being played."

Public Hold'em came to Toronto in March of 1995 and was an instant, raging success. With 11 players almost always seated, and players' pockets bulging with cash, the tables are packed from 12 noon until four in the morning. The charity casino operators grow fat from raking (raping) $10 per hand in 10-20, and $7.50 in 5-10. The government, rather than protecting the consumer, mandated a 5% rake to a maximum of $10. It's for charity isn't it?? Anyone who can play **ABC** poker makes money; those who can play **ABZ** make even more.

Back to that **maniac**. Most often, he will

be from one of the **luck-oriented cultures**, and for some reason, he usually owns a restaurant; Toronto has a lot of restaurants. He'll raise and reraise with hands that a knowledgeable player would have dropped. The pots will get huge. You'll be in there with your pocket Kings and you won't have a chance. Often, it will be seven way, or even a family pot, that erupts with action and is capped before the flop (three raises), or as we say in T.O, "**cappucino.**" After the flop, almost no level of raising can narrow the field as long as there's some hope: a backdoor flush, an inside straight, lowest pair, or hang on until the turn to see if you can pick up a draw. You may have been leading before the flop, but the **Run-Down-Squad** (RDS) has been activated. And in the end, you'll be wearing tire tracks while a maniac rakes in a pot after getting an inside straight draw on the turn and making it on the river. The maniac has two thousand dollars in chips; an hour later he's all in, and you're no longer stuck. Welcome to Toronto, the new and temporary home of longshot poker, where the improbable often triumphs over the probable.

But there are reasonable people here, and some casinos offer a session fee option so that you can play for a much more reasonable $5 per half hour. This turns off some players (uninformed gamblers) because they reason they might not win a pot, so why pay session. Well, that's Toronto.

FINAL PROBABILITY PROBLEM
The following problem is one which was described to me by a friend, local poker legend, Frank G. It's an example of why

I call Toronto the new and temporary home of longshot poker, and it also presents an interesting probability problem which improves our reasoning ability.

LONGSHOT POKER

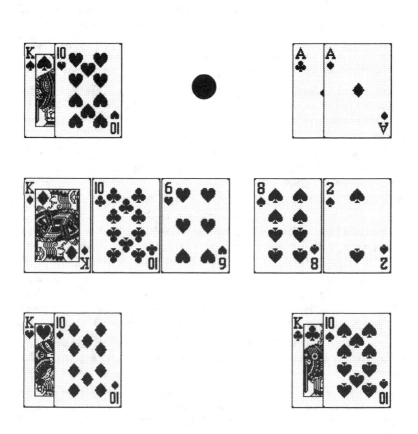

191

A player next to the big blind raised with pocket Aces. He watched bemusedly, as three players called the raise cold. He and the three cold callers were the only ones to see the flop. The flop came KT6, different suits, and there was action like crazy, but not from the player with pocket Aces. The turn was an 8, and the river was a deuce, no flush possible. After the final bets, three players turned over KT **offsuit**, and the pot was split three ways. Someone asked what the odds were of something like that happening, i.e., a K and T on the flop without an Ace, when three players were holding KT offsuit, and a wag replied, "In Toronto, pretty good."

Let's see if we can solve this one. But first, I'm going to ask you to allow me to disregard the pocket Aces for the pre-flop probabilities. Why? Believe me, I ain't tryin' to duck nuthin'. But, to properly calculate the odds against the players getting their starting hands with the pocket Aces **included**, I would have to know how the cards came out one by one, and calculate those individual probabilities. To find out **that** sequence, I would have to have access to the 'Hold'em Hand History Book', in the sky, or, down under, whichever the case may be. Access denied. **But**, if we disregard the pocket Aces, we **can** determine the probability of three players getting KT offsuit, as a fait accompli. The resulting error will be a **slight understatement** of that probability. Thank you.

Now, what is the probability that three players will hold KT offsuit? The number of combinations which can be made from the four Ks and four Ts is 8*7/2*1= 28. Twelve of those are KK and TT combinations (six each), leaving 28-12= 16 KT combinations. Four of those combinations are onsuit, leaving 16-4= 12 offsuit combinations. The probability that the first player will hold KT offsuit is 12/1326= 2/221.

For the second player, there are 50 cards remaining, with three Ks and three Ts, six in all. The number of **two card** combinations from 50 cards is 50*49/2*1= 2450/2= 1225. The number of combinations from six cards is 6*5/2*1= 15. Three Ks can make 3*2/2*1= 3 KK combinations. The three Ts also make three TT combinations. The number of KT combinations is 15-6= 9. With two suits gone, the number of onsuit KT combinations is two, leaving 9-2= 7 offsuit KT combinations. The probability that the second player will have KT offsuit is 7/1225. **Assume** that the KT which the second player gets are the two suits not in the KT held by the first player, i.e., if the first player holds KcTs, the second player holds KhTd.

For the third player, there are 48 cards remaining, with two Ks and two Ts- four cards in all. The number of two card combinations from 48 cards is 48*47/2*1= 2256/2= 1128. The number of two card combinations from the four cards is 4*3/2*1= 6. Two of those combinations are KK and TT, leaving 4 KT offsuit combinations. The probability that the third player will have KT offsuit is 4/1128= 1/282.

The probability of three players holding KT offsuit is 2/221*7/1225*1/282= 14/76,344,450= 1/5,453,175, or odds against of 5,453,174:1. But the story is not over.

Now, we need to determine the probability

of the flop containing a KT i.e., the sole remaining K and T. The total possible number of flops with 44 cards (52 less three Ks, less three Ts, less the two Aces) is 44*43*42/3*2*1= 13244. The remaining KT combination can have as its third card, any card from the remaining ranks, except the two Aces. That number is 10*4=40 cards. Therefore, the number of KT combos is 40, and the probability of that happening is 40/13244= 10/3311.

The combined probability of three players holding KT offsuit, and having the flop come KTx, where x is any card but an Ace is 1/5,453,175*10/3311, and that's a real longshot.

It might be tempting to try and solve this problem by combining probabilities along the following lines: the probability of hitting a King is 4/52. The probability that the second player will receive a King is 3/52, etc. Stop there. It cannot be done. What we are actually doing by this process is determining the probability of the cards coming in a very specific order: KKK and then TTT, and that is a very different and even more improbable proposition than three players ending up with KT offsuit. Using our approach with combinations, the cards could have come in any order such as TKKKTT, etc. We could also try the probability of hitting either a K or a T, but this would not ensure that the players received KT as opposed to KK or TT. Once again, only combinations can solve a difficult problem such as the one we just went through.

FINAL DISCUSSION

In light of the previous situation, it seems appropriate to end this book by a discussion of something which most of us will have experienced or observed- the phenomenon of **persistent improbability**. In the following paragraphs, I will define what I mean by this, offer what I consider to be a plausible (hopefully) explanation, and offer some ways in which to handle it.

By improbability, I do **not** mean losing to legitimate hands, or the occasional longshot hand heads-up, or a gaggle of players whose individual hand probabilities for improvement are low, but whose sum of probabilities is high, such that **one** of them wins, and **you** lose. But, I **do** mean when you start finding yourself in these situations **persistently**, and losing **persistently**, such as in the following situations:

a) you raise in early position with pocket Aces and five players call the raise cold. You lose the hand.

b) you raise in early position with pocket Kings and are re-raised by pocket Aces. You lose.

c) you have a flush draw (nine outs) against someone's straight draw (six outs). You lose.

d) you have a flush draw. You miss it. You have more flush draws. You miss them.

e) you have an open-ended straight draw against someone's inside straight draw. You lose to someone who has your number.

f) you have pocket Aces, raise, and are called by someone heads-up with 3 and 4 of clubs. He makes the flush, you lose.

A few things are happening here. **Every**

time you have a good hand and try to narrow down the field, too many other players **coincidentally** have hands they want to play, or, they just plain hate your guts. When you have a great hand like pocket Ks, someone **coincidentally** has a greater hand- pocket Aces. When you're drawing to a heart flush, the deck **coincidentally** changes direction and backdoors someone with spades. When you have a big draw against someone's smaller draw, the deck has been shuffled (stacked) **coincidentally** in the other player's favor, so that their card comes. And here you're the best player at the table and a favorite to win! Many authors tell you to hang in until the cards change, but, you're losing a fortune. What's going on?

You are experiencing '**persistent negative coincidence**' (**PNC**). You are playing well, doing everything right, but can't overcome **PNC**. What can you do?

I can suggest the following: wait for a dealer change, request a deck change, have the cards washed frequently to restore proportionality, change tables, change limits, take a walk, change cardrooms. If these don't work, **go home** and sleep that night with a chicken underneath your pillow to change your **coincidence**. Just kidding.

Why does it happen? Is it the revenge of the poker gods? I don't know why it happens, except that it **does** happen, and the sooner you can recognize that it's a **PNC** day, the better- for your mental health and your bankroll. Of course, **PNC** happens to me more often than to other players. Really! Most other players experience **PPC**, persistent positive coincidence, i.e., they make their hand whenever they have the worst of it. I don't experience **PPC**. I know, because my losses pay for their nice lifestyles. So please, if you've found this book useful and/or entertaining, tell your friends to buy a copy so that I can continue to play. I'm sure that my first ever **PPC** day is just around the corner. By the way, my poem, **A Gambler's Lament**, at the end of this book, contains both **PPC** and **PNC**.

A FEW FINAL THOUGHTS

Having absorbed the material in this book, you now have a probabilistic expectation for all the types of starting hands, from flop to finish. How will it affect your play? Let's put some starting hands into perspective.

For the pocket pair, the probability of flopping 'at least a set', is about 12%. The big pocket pairs, As, Ks, and Qs, are hands in themselves; if they don't improve on the flop, they still have a good chance of winning. With the lower pairs, drawing hands in a way, you either improve, have some kind of straight draw, chase, or, most often, release in the face of action when higher cards flop; and most often, as we have seen, higher cards **will** flop. Therefore, for the lower pairs, and speaking from a pot odds point of view, you will want many players in the pot: ideally, 7.5 dollars for every one of yours. This approach, carried out consistently, will offset the disadvantage of going in with the weaker pocket pairs.

For suited cards, the probability of flopping a flush is .84%- negligible. The probability of flopping a four flush is about 11%, or odds against of **8:1**. If you look down and see two suited cards whose potential is primarily making a flush, you want many callers. **Most often**, it is much better to go with a hand that has flush and straight potential, i.e., suited connectors. If the cards are of the higher ranks, you also have better 'winning pair potential', and a pair wins many hands, in all but the loosest of games. Also, think twice about calling a good player's raise when you hold a hand like AT suited. Often, you're drawing a lot thinner than you think you are.

For starting hands of different ranks, the probability of flopping a pair is 29%. The probability of flopping two pair is 2%, or odds against of **49:1**. If you're playing 69 offsuit, you're asking Lady Luck to marry you. When playing cards of different ranks, favor the higher connectors that give straight and big pair potential.

You will have noticed that most hands are never a favorite to improve. The one exception is the four flush **and** open-ended straight draw with two cards to come, and only slightly. In the **Foreword** to this book, I proposed that an intimate knowledge of probability might keep you from going on tilt. You have it, and this may be the greatest benefit of this book. So, keep your cool the next time the flop completely misses your AK suited. You never were, oddly speaking, a favorite to hit something.

Finally, all of this is old hat to good players who know the rules and the exceptions; for the novice, it may come as revelation. The last few words: a bird in the hand is worth two in the bush, and a big pair wins more often than a draw. In other words, limit Hold'em is most often a big card game. Good luck and adios.

PART III

Solutions

&

Poem

SOLUTIONS TO QUIZZES

MATH REVIEW
1. (1225-1081)/1225= 144/1225= .118
2. **16/1326**= 8/663= .012. **2304/19600**= 144/1225= .118
3. 50*49*48/3*2*1= 19600.
4. 52*51*50*49*48/5*4*3*2*1= 2,598,960.
5. .35*100= 35% and .0084*100= .84%
6. 31.5%/100= .315 and .03%/100= .0003
7. 1.86= 1.9 and 2.76= 2.8
8. x/1326= 1/221 and 221x= 1326 and x= 1326/221= 6;
u*969=15504*64 and u= 15504*64/969= 992256/969= 1024.

ODDS AND PROBABILITIES
The probability of getting a pocket pair as your hole cards is 1/17. The odds against getting a pocket pair are 16:1. The odds against getting at least a set on the flop are 7.5:1. The probability of improving to at least a set is 1/8.5= 11.8%. With an open-ended straight draw and one card to come, you have eight outs in the remaining 46 cards. The odds against making the straight are (46-8):8= 38:8= 4.8:1. The probability of making the straight is 1/5.8= 17.3%. The probability of getting suited cards before the flop is 23.5%. The odds against it are (100-23.5):23.5= 76.5:23.5= 3.3:1. The odds against flopping a flush are 118:1. The probability of it happening is 1/119= .84%.

COMBINATIONS
1. The total possible number of five card flushes which can be made from the 13 spades is 13*12*11*10*9/5*4*3*2*1= 154440/120= 1287.

2. The total possible number of five card combinations which can be made from 50 cards is 50*49*48*47*46/5*4*3*2*1= 2,118,760.

SIMPLE PROBABILITIES

1. With two cards to come, there are 47 cards remaining. The total possible number of two card combinations is 47*46/2*1= 1081. With four outs, you can make your hand by hitting either one out, or hitting both outs. Putting the four outs aside, there are 47-4= 43 cards which do not help your hand. Either of the four outs may combine with either of these 43 cards, giving 4*43= 172 one out combinations. The number of two out combinations is 4*3/2*1= 6. The total number of combinations which complete your hand is 172+6= 178. The probability of making your hand is 178/1081= 16.5%.

2. If you hold two suited cards, there are 50 cards remaining. The total possible number of three card combinations which can be made from 50 cards is 50*49*48/3*2*1= 19600. The number of suited cards remaining is 13-2= 11. To flop a flush, three of your suit must fall. The total possible number of three card combinations of your suit is 11*10*9/3*2*1= 165. The probability of flopping a flush is 165/19600= .0084= .84%.

3. The probability of flopping quad Queens when holding AQ is 1/19600= .005%.

COMPLEX PROBABILITIES

1. By definition, trips are two of a kind on the flop, that match one of your hole cards. With two hole cards, it is possible to flop two kinds of trips, and with 50 cards remaining, the total possible number of

three cards flops is 50*49*48/3*2*1= 19600. For each hole card, there are three more of the same rank remaining. The number of two card combinations which the three remaining cards of each rank can make is 3*2/2*1= 3. Either of those two card combinations may combine with any of the remaining cards which will not produce a full house, i.e., match your other hole card. The remaining cards are 50-3-3= 44. For your one hole card, the number of trip combinations is 3*44= 132. The same will be true for the other card. The number of combinations which give only trips is 132+132= 264. The probability of flopping trips is 264/19600= 1.35= 1.4%.

2. With one Ace flashed and no longer available, there is only one Ace left with which to flop a set, or Aces full. The number of remaining cards is 49. The total possible number of three card combinations (flops) is 49*48*47/3*2*1= 18424. There are 48 non-Ace cards remaining, making the total possible number of two card combinations equal to 48*47/2*1= 1128. The lone remaining Ace may combine with either of the 1128 two card combinations. The probability of flopping a set of Aces, or Aces full is 1128/18424= .06= 6%.

3. To determine the total possible number of full houses, we need to determine the number of three of a kinds which any rank can make, and determine the number of pairs which any rank can make. The number of three of a kinds which any rank can make is 4*3*2/3*2*1= 24/6= 4. The number of pairs which any rank can make is 4*3/2*1= 6. For deuces full for example, there are three 222 combinations. Those three combinations may

combine with any pair from the remaining 12 ranks. The number of pairs from the remaining 12 ranks is 6*12= 72. The number of deuces full is 4*72= 288. The same will be true for any other rank. The total number of full houses is 13*288= 3744.

4. The correct answer to **Petriv's Paradox** is **2,598,960**. While it is true that for each two card starting hand there are 19600 different flops, this is true only when looked at in isolation. Many of those five card hands repeat themselves with different starting hands, i.e., they are common to other starting hands. To give an example, take 2c2s. The flop might come 2d2hAc, or one of the other 19599 possible combinations. But, if the next time your starting cards are 2d2h, the flop might come 2c2sAc, which gives the same five card hand as our first starting hand, 2c2s. We have begun to repeat hands. After all the repeating hands are stripped out, there will be only 2,598,960 uniquely different five card hands.

5. When holding AQ of clubs, the number of clubs remaining is 11. The total number of two club combinations is 11*10/2*1= 55. There are three Aces and three Queens remaining, either of which may combine with either of the 55 two club combinations. The probability of flopping a four flush and a pair is 6*55/19600= 330/19600= .017= 1.7%. The odds against it are (19600-330):330= 19270:330= 58:1. For the probability of completing the flush, or improving to two pairs or trips, see the annexes, **SUITED CARDS**, and **OFFSUIT CARDS**, respectively.

6. Solution to flopping one of the hands depicted below with AK of spades.

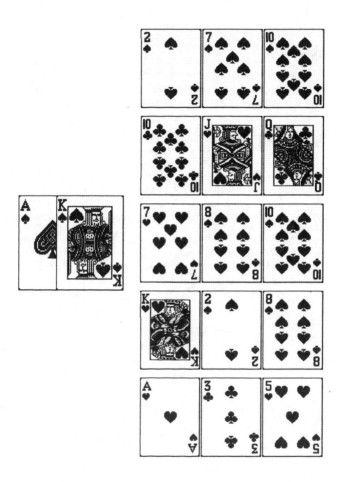

By hands:
Flopping a flush. With AK of spades in your hand, there are 11 spades remaining. To flop a flush, a three spade combination must fall. The number of three spade combinations which can be made from 11 spades, and

therefore, flop the flush is, $11*10*9/3*2*1=$ $990/6= 165$.

Flopping a straight. With AK of spades, the cards which flop a straight are TJQ. The number of TJQ sequences which can be made from all the Ts, Js, and Qs is 64 (see **REFERENCE COMBINATIONS**, work on 789). One of those 64 combinations is the TJQ of spades and has already been accounted for in flopping a flush. Therefore, there are 63 combinations which flop a straight.

Flopping a four flush only. With 11 spades remaining, the number of two spade combinations which can be made is $11*10/2*1=$ 55. Each of those two spade combinations may combine with either of the 33 remaining cards which do not produce a pair or a three spade combination (52 minus four As, minus four Ks, minus the two spade combination, minus the other nine spades). The number of combinations which flop a four flush only is $55*33= 1815$. There is one slight problem. Look at the following: TsJsQcdh, TsJcdhQs, and TcdhJsQs. These two spade combinations produce straights, and we have already accounted for all the straight making combinations. The number of these straight making combinations is nine, and these will have to be subtracted from 1815, leaving **1806** combinations.

Flopping a four flush and a pair. As per the solution for AQ of clubs, the number of combinations is 330.

Flopping a pair. There are three Aces and three Kings remaining. The model for a pair is Axy, or Kxy, where xy are any two cards which are not an A or a K, and where xy is not a two spade combination. The number of cards which xy is drawn from is 44. The number of two card combinations which can be made from 44 cards is 44*43/2*1= 946. Some of those 946 combinations are two spade combinations which need to be stripped out. The number of two spade combinations is 11*10/2*1= 55. Therefore, the number of xy combinations which are not two spades is 946-55= 891. The number of combinations which contain only a pair and not a four flush is 6*891= 5346.

Summary. The probability of flopping one of the hands is the sum of the combinations over 19600, i.e., (165+63+1806+330+5346) /19600= 7710/19600= .393= 39.3%.

Note that we have not included the combinations which flop two pair (396 combinations), trips (264) , a full house (18) and quads (2), for an additional 680 combinations (numbers from the annex, **OFFSUIT CARDS**). This gives a final probability of flopping some kind of hand as (7710+680)/19600= 8390/19600= **42.8%**.

You are a dog to outflop pocket deuces with AK suited. If you have missed the flop, you have a 24% probability, or odds against of 3:1, to hit one or two of your six outs to make a pair, two pairs, or trips by the river (**TABLE OF TWO TO COME**). Why play AK? Because pot odds are usually greater than your odds against improving.

Part of the purpose of this exercise, aside from the detailed methodology employed, is to keep you from going on tilt when your starting, premium drawing hands completely miss the flop. As we have just seen, it is probable that they will do so. In the annexes, you will be exposed to these same methodologies again, so that it will become a familiar approach to solutions.

A GAMBLER'S LAMENT

I remember when the cards turned generously,
I loved, I laughed, I lived gloriously,
the skies were blue, I drank of honeydew,
and thanked Fate for rendering me my due.

I came to expect a life of leisure,
with lucky play as my means to treasure,
and higher limits only increased my win,
much to the skilled card players' chagrin.

Self-declared, a poker prince with crown,
I paid no heed to losers gathered 'round,
for I was anointed, Lady Luck's creation,
freed from odds and negative expectation.

Ominously, the women began to drift away,
quick to sense when a man's had his day,
and then the inside straights never hit-
even flush draws became a bottomless pit.

I spiralled downward into deeper oblivion
and prayed to escape from luck's dominion,
but my arrogance broke me, a crying clown,
to become one of the losers gathered 'round.

Now humbled, I befriend one and all,
lackey to those with money on call,
but my sun has set, no coming dawn,
to rue unearned glory, fleeting and gone.

Mike Petriv
October 1994

NOTES